SCHOLASTIC

READ180

rBook™

Stage A

No part of this publication may be reproduced in whole or in part, or stored in a retrieval system, or transmitted in any form or by any means, electronic, mechanical, photocopying, recording, or otherwise, without written permission of the publisher. For information regarding permission, write to Scholastic Inc., 557 Broadway, New York, NY 10012. Acknowledgments and credits appear on pages 277–278, which constitute an extension of this copyright page.

Copyright © 2005 by Scholastic Inc.

All rights reserved.   Published by Scholastic Inc.   Printed in the U.S.A.
ISBN 0-439-67077-2
SCHOLASTIC, READ 180, and associated logos and designs are trademarks and/or registered trademarks of Scholastic Inc.

7   8   9   10   14   14 13 12 11 10 09 08 07

Table of Contents

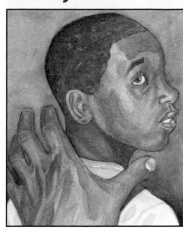

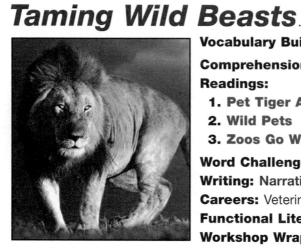

Nonfiction and Literature

No Small Hero

Welcome to the rBook

Get ready for the rBook by taking this quiz. After you finish each Workshop, check back to see if your ideas or opinions have changed.

1 Fires Out of Control

A huge fire is headed toward your neighborhood. Read the following statements. Check which one you think is right.

❑ You should stay at home and protect your house from the fire.

❑ You should leave your house and go with your family to a shelter.

2 Coming to America

Why do you think people move to the U.S. from other countries? Order the reasons below.

1 = most common reason
4 = least common reason

—— People want to go to U.S. schools.

—— People like American food.

—— People have to leave their homes because of violence and war.

—— People want to start a new life in a country with a lot of freedom.

3 Bud, Not Buddy

Bud, Not Buddy is a story about a kid who has to fend for himself. Bud learns a lot by being on his own. Read the statements below. Check the ones you think will be true for Bud.

❑ Everyone tries to help a poor kid.

❑ People like to share what they have.

❑ It's easy for a kid to get by on his own.

4 Bullies Beware

At lunch, a bully at your table is harassing another student. What do you do? Circle your answer.

1. I would tell an adult.

2. I would tell the bully to leave the student alone.

3. I would keep quiet so that the bully wouldn't say anything to me.

5 Secrets of the Mummy's Tomb

Think about the Workshop title, "Secrets of the Mummy's Tomb." Look at the photo below. What do you predict this Workshop will be about? Explain your answer.

_____

_____

_____

_____

6 Good Sports

Read the statements about sports below. Write **A** if you agree. Write **D** if you disagree.

—— Everyone has at least one sport or activity they are good at.

—— Playing games like marbles isn't very competitive.

—— If you aren't naturally talented at sports, practicing won't help you.

7 Taming Wild Beasts

Which of these animals would make a good pet? Check them.

❑ tiger cub ❑ bird

❑ bear cub ❑ elephant

❑ dog ❑ alligator

❑ cat ❑ gorilla

Circle the pet (if any) you'd like to have.

8 Food: The Good, the Bad, and the Gross

What do you think you'll be reading about in this Workshop? Write down one food in each column.

Good Food	Bad Food	Gross Food

What is your favorite food?

_____

_____

Is it healthy?

❑ yes ❑ no ❑ I don't know

9 No Small Hero

Who is someone you think is a hero? _____

What could a kid do to become a hero?

_____

_____

_____

Comprehension Focus
Main Idea and Details

FIRES
Out of Control

Every year, wildfires burn through America's forests. Red-hot flames turn trees into blackened poles. Hot, dry winds blow sparks across hundreds of acres. And when wildfires reach towns, people run for their lives.

In this Workshop, you'll find out what it's like to survive a wildfire. You'll meet fire-fighting heroes. You'll also discover the explosive science behind fire.

Turn the page and get ready—the heat is on!

VOCABULARY BUILDER

◉ Target Word ▶ Read the Target Words. Rate each one using the scale below.*	Meaning ▶ Read the Target Word meanings. Write in the missing ones.	Example ▶ Finish the Target Word examples below. Fill in the missing ones.
degree de•gree (noun) ① ② ③		Firefighters wear jackets that resist heat up to 700 **degrees**! 
fuel fu•el (noun) ① ② ③	something that can be burned	
rapidly rap•id•ly (adverb) ① ② ③		Ways of getting around rapidly include . . .
region re•gion (noun) ① ② ③	an area of some place, like a state or country	
survive sur•vive (verb) ① ② ③		To survive a fire, I would . . .

*Rating Scale

① = I don't know it at all.
② = I've seen it before.
③ = I know it and use it.

I Survived the Yellowstone Fire

by Zoë Kashner

Deer flee the Yellowstone fire.

In 1988, when I was 13, my family went to Yellowstone National Park. We didn't go to camp. We went to see the biggest fire in the history of the park.

We heard about the fire on the way back from a camping trip. My dad was a science teacher. He thought we should see this once-in-a-lifetime fire. We took a vote. Dad won. So, we drove to Montana.

We were allowed to enter the park. It was amazing. Driving in, we saw bears fleeing the flames. Smoke filled the air. We made it to the center of the park.

Everything seemed under control. Then we heard bad news. Park rangers told us that taking the road out was too risky. We were trapped inside the park for the night! We had to share a tent with two other families. I had a hard time sleeping. Would the fire **approach** our tent? Would I ever see my home again?

In the morning, the rangers let us drive out of the park. We were safe. In fact, no one died in that fire.

When the fire finally burned out, over 1.2 million acres were burned to the ground. I'm glad I got to see the fire. I'm also glad that we made it out alive! *END*

Words to Know! | **fleeing** running away

💡 The Big Idea

Write What is this article mainly about?

_____

_____

_____

VOCABULARY BUILDER

◎ Target Word

approach
ap•proach (verb)

Rate it: ① ② ③

Meaning

_____

_____

Example

_____

_____

_____

❗ React

What might be scary about seeing a wildfire up close? What might be interesting?

Main Idea and Details

The **main idea** is the most important point about a topic. **Details** are the facts that support the main idea. To find the main idea and details:

- Decide what the topic is. Find the main idea about the topic.
- Look for the details that support the main idea.

▶ **Fill in this chart with the main idea and details of "I Survived the Yellowstone Fire."**

Detail

Zoë's dad thought the family should see the once-in-a-lifetime fire.

Detail

_____

_____

_____

_____

Main Idea

_____

_____

_____

_____

_____

Detail

_____

_____

_____

_____

Detail

_____

_____

_____

_____

SMOKE

Smoke jumpers prepare to stop a fire.

💡 The Big Idea

Write ▷ What is this article mainly about?

_____

_____

_____

VOCABULARY BUILDER

◎ Target Word

condition
con•di•tion *(noun)*

Rate it: ① ② ③

Meaning

_____

_____

Example

_____

_____

_____

❗ React

Would you be afraid to jump out of a plane with a parachute? Why or why not?

JUMPERS

Most people run from fires. These heroes jump into the flames.

Who do people call when forest fires start? Smoke jumpers. They are special firefighters. Their job is hot and tough. But it's very important.

Tough Work

Smoke jumping is a challenging job. Not just anyone can do it. Smoke jumpers have to be smart and physically fit. They must brave dangerous **conditions** when they work.

Smoke jumpers go where other firefighters can't. Many fires start deep in the woods. Without roads, trucks can't help. Instead, jumpers are dropped from planes. All their assistance must come from the air.

Safety First

Staying safe is important for smoke jumpers. Safety starts in the air. When they drop out of the planes, smoke jumpers steer their parachutes. They have to land away from the flames.

On the ground, the danger heats up rapidly. Smoke jumpers can get trapped. So, they wear clothes that won't burn. They also carry tents that won't catch on fire. That way, they can hide inside the tents. They can sweat it out until the fire passes. ➔

Words to Know!   **assistance**   help

Main Idea and Details

1. **Write** Find the main idea in the section "Tough Work."

_____

_____

_____

_____

_____

2. **Underline** Find two important details that support the main idea in "Tough Work."

3. **Write** Find the main idea in the section "Safety First."

_____

_____

_____

_____

_____

4. **Underline** Find two important details that support the main idea in "Safety First."

A smoke jumper prepares to parachute into a burning forest.

❂ Active Reading

Underline ▶ What do smoke jumpers do when they can't put out a fire?

VOCABULARY BUILDER
◎ Target Word

locate

lo•cate (verb)

Rate it: ① ② ③

Meaning

_____

_____

Example

_____

_____

_____

❶ React

Write ▶ What would be cool about being a smoke jumper? What might not be so cool?

_____

_____

_____

Getting the Job Done

How do smoke jumpers do their job? They don't have big hoses. They don't have huge trucks. But they know other ways to fight fire.

Sometimes, smoke jumpers fight fire with fire. How? They start a "back burn." This method burns the trees in the fire's path. Then the fire has no fuel to burn. The fire can't spread.

Some jumpers dig a ditch to stop a fire. The ditch is called a "fire line." To make the fire line, jumpers cut down trees. They also dig up bushes. Finally, a big dirt ditch divides the region on fire from the rest of the forest. When the fire reaches the ditch, there's nothing to burn. So it stops spreading.

Smoke jumpers also get help from above. How? Planes scoop up water from a lake. Then, they fly over the fire. When the pilot **locates** the fire, they dump the water. Whoosh! The fire goes out.

If nothing else works, jumpers have to wait for rain. Rain can put a fire out for good.

Smoke jumping is very exciting. But this career is far from easy. The next time you hear about a forest fire, you'll know the heroes who are coming to the rescue—the smoke jumpers. _END_

Words to Know!	**method** way of doing something

Main Idea and Details

▶ Fill in this chart with the main idea and details in "Getting the Job Done."

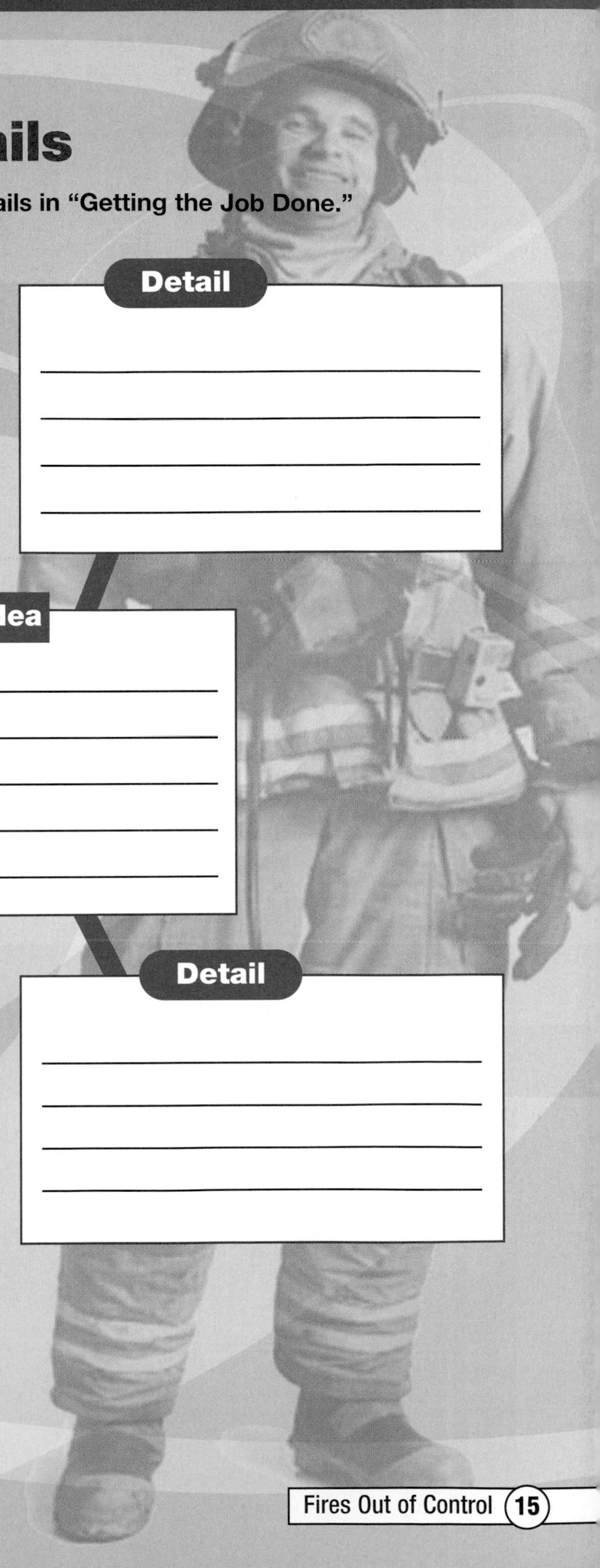

Detail

_____

_____

_____

_____

Detail

_____

_____

_____

_____

Main Idea

_____

_____

_____

_____

_____

Detail

_____

_____

_____

_____

Detail

_____

_____

_____

_____

The Big Idea

Write What is this article mainly about?

_____

_____

_____

VOCABULARY BUILDER

Target Word

rebuild
re•build (verb)

Rate it: ① ② ③

Meaning

_____

_____

Example

_____

_____

_____

React

What things would you want to take with you if your house was on fire?

Up in FLAMES

Flames from the California fires light up the night.

What happens when wildfires sweep across 750,000 acres? It's a disaster that's too hot to handle.

A State on Fire

In 2003, the foothills of Southern California went up in flames. The first fire began in early October. Within days, 14,000 firefighters were battling a dozen blazes! Sometimes, there was little they could do. They could only watch as flames destroyed homes and jumped over freeways.

In the end, more than 20 people died. Almost 3,000 houses burned down.

Why were people at such risk from the fires? It's

because many homes are in the foothills. They are surrounded by trees. There are only a few windy roads to get out.

Fire Survivors

In many places, people escaped early. Firefighters went door-to-door. They told people to leave their homes for safety.

People went to friends' homes or hotels. Shelters were set up away from the fire. In San Bernardino, almost 2,000 people fled to a huge barn that used to house airplanes.

Others had to rapidly race away from their burning homes. Many drove down roads with flames high on both sides.

But not everyone left home in time. One family found itself trapped. They survived the fire by diving into their swimming pool. The windows of their house exploded in front of them.

The 2003 fires blazed for a month. Then, in November, the rain came. The fires finally fizzled out. But the damage was done. California had to spend $250 million fighting the fires. It would take billions more to **rebuild** lost property. And the 20 lives lost could never be replaced. ➡

Words to Know! **foothills** low hills at the base of mountains

---

📖 **Main Idea and Details**

1. **Write** ▶ Find the main idea in "A State on Fire."

_____

_____

_____

_____

_____

2. **Underline** ▶ Find two important details in that section.

3. **Write** ▶ Find the main idea in "Fire Survivors."

_____

_____

_____

_____

_____

4. **Underline** ▶ Find two important details in that section.

📖 **Review: Read for Detail**

Circle ▶ Find one detail that tells when the fires finally ended.

 Active Reading

Star ▶ How hot can it get during California summers?

VOCABULARY BUILDER
◎ Target Word

challenge
chal•lenge (noun)

Rate it: ① ② ③

Meaning

_____

_____

Example

_____

_____

_____

React

Write ▶ Think about your home. How safe is it from fire?

_____

_____

_____

How Fires Start

The wildfires of 2003 could happen again. California has all the necessary conditions for fires to go out of control. It has fuel, oxygen, and heat.

Fuel is anything that can burn easily. Dry trees, leaves, logs, or twigs are fuel. A common fuel in California is thick brush called chaparral. Chaparral burns quickly at high-degree temperatures. It grows over most of the California foothills.

Fires also need oxygen. Oxygen is part of the air. Wind feeds a fire extra oxygen. This makes the fire burn hotter. Wind can also help a fire spread. Places that are windy often suffer more fire damage. California is very windy. The Santa Ana winds, which come every fall, are very strong.

The last thing a fire needs is heat. Sun and warm weather create heat. California is famous for its sunshine. In the summer, the temperature often hits 100 degrees.

TEXT FEATURE: **Reading a Diagram**

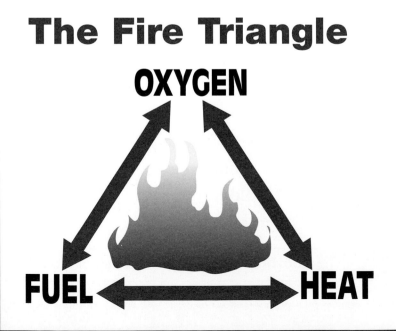

The Fire Triangle
OXYGEN
FUEL   HEAT

Fires Vs. Firefighters

Saving homes from wildfires is a **challenge**. Firefighters have little warning when fires are coming. They must work fast to save what they can.

First, firefighters will survey a town. They will mark houses "winners" and "losers." A log cabin surrounded by shrubs is a loser. It has a lot of fuel for the fire and probably can't be saved. Firefighters mark losers with red tape on the door.

To save a house, firefighters make a "defensible space." That's an area around the house without fuel. This becomes a barrier. Then, they bulldoze around towns and houses, creating a gap the fire can't jump.

Then the fire hits. Some houses will burn to the ground. Others will remain untouched. Why? Often, the wind or weather changes directions. In addition, some houses are made out of non-flammable materials. Others are highly flammable.

Once the fire is out, people can begin to rebuild. But the fear of next year's fires still remains. (END)

Words to Know!	**defensible** able to defend

A diagram is a drawing or plan that explains something.

1. According to this diagram, what do fires need to burn?
   - Ⓐ fuel
   - Ⓑ fuel and oxygen
   - Ⓒ fuel, oxygen, and heat
   - Ⓓ oxygen and heat

2. What happens if you remove oxygen from a fire?
   - Ⓐ It burns brighter.
   - Ⓑ It goes out.
   - Ⓒ It turns into gold.
   - Ⓓ It burns hotter.

3. Why is this diagram called "The Fire Triangle"?

_____

Main Idea and Details

1. **Write** Find the main idea in "How Fires Start."

_____

_____

_____

_____

_____

2. **Underline** Find two important details in that section.

Skills Check

1. **Write** Find the main idea in "Fires Vs. Firefighters."

_____

_____

_____

_____

_____

2. **Underline** Find two important details in that section.

Take the WORD CHALLENGE

1 Number them. How rapidly would each food below disappear from your fridge?

1 = most rapidly   4 = least rapidly

____ leftover pizza

____ leftover mac-n-cheese

____ leftover birthday cake

____ cat food

- - - -

2 Identify them. Read the list below. Circle the three places that are regions (not cities or states).

Texas

Chicago, IL

The Great Plains

The Northwest

California

The East Coast

New York, NY

3 Prefixes

A **prefix** is a letter or a group of letters added to the beginning of a word. A prefix changes the meaning of a word. The prefix *re-* means "again." So *redo* means "to do again." *Redial* means to "dial again."

Define. All these words have the prefix *re-*. Guess what the words mean, based on the meaning of the prefix. Then check a dictionary.

Meaning

1. recount   _____

2. reuse   _____

3. reread   _____

4. rejoin   _____

> One more hit, and our rivals will **regain** their lead!

4 Analyze. Which items might you wear outside if the temperature were 20 degrees? Check one or more.

☐ scarf   ☐ T-shirt   ☐ mittens   ☐ sandals

What if the temperature were 99 degrees? Check the items you might wear.

☐ ski cap   ☐ flip-flops   ☐ shorts   ☐ sweater

- - - - - - - - -

5 Rank them. Which of the following would use the most fuel? Rank them from 1 to 3.

1 = the least fuel   3 = the most fuel

_____ a plane trip from New York to LA

_____ mowing your front lawn

_____ a boat pulling two water skiiers

6 **Check them.** Read the events below. Which ones might cause someone to rebuild a house?

☐ a busy yard sale

☐ a huge tornado

☐ a light rain

☐ a major flood

---

7 **Analyze.** What are the best weather conditions to do these outdoor activities?

fly a kite: _____

build a snowman: _____

swim at the beach: _____

ride a bike: _____

8 **Suffixes**

A **suffix** is a letter or a group of letters added to the end of a word. A suffix changes the meaning or part of speech of a word. The suffixes –er and –or mean "a person or thing connected with." These suffixes turn verbs into nouns. *Drive* is a verb. *Driver* is a noun.

Turn these verbs into nouns by adding the suffix -er.

read: _____

bank: _____

work: _____

Now turn these verbs into nouns by adding the suffix -or.

sail: _____

survive: _____

investigate: _____

9 **Discuss.** What's a really good way to approach a new kid at school?

_____

_____

What's a really bad way to approach a new kid at school?

_____

_____

10 **Fill in.** Complete the blanks with locate, survive, and challenge.

I wasn't sure I would _____ my first day at a new school. First, it was a real _____ to open my locker. Then I couldn't _____ the lunch room. When I did, the lunch was gross!

FINISH

This **reader** reads books using a special alphabet for the blind called Braille.

Writing Focus

Expository Paragraph

An expository paragraph gives information about a topic.

▶ **Read Julia's expository paragraph about the job of a forest ranger.**

Student Model

Keeping Forests Safe

by Julia Rodriguez

Being a forest ranger is a challenging job. To start with, forest rangers must be physically fit. They have to walk many miles every day and often have to rebuild trails and campsites. In addition, forest rangers have to know a lot about the region where they work. Most rangers can identify all the plants and animals in their forests. Most importantly, rangers must keep campers safe. They protect campers if a fire or storm approaches. In conclusion, being a forest ranger is a challenging job that is very important.

Parts of an Expository Paragraph

▶ **Find these parts of Julia's expository paragraph.**

1. Underline the sentence that states the **topic**.
2. Check three important **details** that support or explain the topic.
3. Notice the **order** of the details.
4. Circle the **linking words** that connect the details.
5. Put a star beside the sentence that **sums up** or restates the topic.

Brainstorm

▶ Read the writing prompt in the middle of the idea web. Then use the boxes to help you brainstorm your ideas.

Things Firefighters Do

Things Firefighters Know

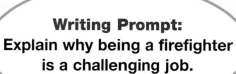

Writing Prompt:
Explain why being a firefighter is a challenging job.

Dangers Firefighters Face

Equipment Firefighters Use

Expository Paragraph | **Plan**

Plan Your Paragraph

Writing Prompt: Explain why being a firefighter is a challenging job.

▶ Use this chart to plan and organize your paragraph.

Word Choices

_____

_____

_____

_____

_____

Topic Sentence

- *Being a firefighter is . . .*

- *Fighting fires is . . .*

- *A really tough job is . . .*

First Detail

- *To start with, . . .*

- *One difficulty is . . .*

- *First of all, . . .*

Second Detail

- *In addition, . . .*

- *Also, . . .*

- *On the other hand, . . .*

Third Detail

- *Most importantly, . . .*

- *Finally, . . .*

- *Also, . . .*

Conclusion

- *In conclusion, . . .*

- *To sum it up, . . .*

- *Overall, . . .*

Write Your Paragraph

▶ Use this writing frame to write a first draft of your paragraph.

_____
(title)

Being a firefighter is _____

_____

_____

To start with, _____

_____

_____

In addition, _____

_____

_____

Most importantly, _____

_____

_____

_____

In conclusion, _____

_____

_____

_____

Revise

▶ Rate your paragraph. Then have a writing partner rate it.

Scoring Guide			
weak	okay	good	strong
1	2	3	4

1. Does the first sentence state the **topic**?

Self	1	2	3	4
Partner	1	2	3	4

2. Do **details** support or explain the topic?

Self	1	2	3	4
Partner	1	2	3	4

3. Are the supporting details in a **logical order**?

Self	1	2	3	4
Partner	1	2	3	4

4. Do **linking words** connect the details?

Self	1	2	3	4
Partner	1	2	3	4

5. Does the ending **sum up** or restate the topic?

Self	1	2	3	4
Partner	1	2	3	4

▶ Now revise your paragraph to make it stronger.

Grammar IDENTIFYING SENTENCES AND FRAGMENTS

A **sentence** is a group of words that tells a complete idea. Every sentence has two parts.

- The subject tells who or what the sentence is about.
- The predicate tells what someone or something does.

Example

Subject	Predicate
The bears	escaped the fire.
The raging fires	burned everything around them.

▶ Identify the underlined part of each sentence below. Write **subject** or **predicate** on the line beside it.

1. Smoke jumpers <u>have very dangerous jobs</u>.   *predicate*

2. An airplane <u>carries them to forest fires</u>. _____

3. Then <u>these firefighters</u> leap from airplanes. _____

4. They <u>steer their parachutes away from the flames</u>. _____

5. <u>The heat and smoke</u> make working difficult. _____

6. Sometimes, <u>the firefighters</u> dig fire lines, too. _____

A **sentence fragment** is an incomplete sentence that cannot stand by itself. Often, a fragment is missing either a subject or a predicate.

▶ Rewrite the sentence fragments below as complete sentences.

7. put out many forest fires last year

_____

8. the brave smoke jumpers

_____

9. lots of heavy equipment

_____

10. must be strong, smart, and brave

_____

Edit ▶ *Take a close look at each of the sentences in your draft on page 25. Do they all tell a complete idea? Fix the ones that don't.*

Mechanics USING END PUNCTUATION

Different kinds of sentences use different **end punctuation marks**.

- A statement always ends with a period.
- A question always ends with a question mark.

Example

Statement	Question
Firefighters have to be brave.	Do you know a firefighter?
A fire station is down the street.	Have you ever seen a fire?

▶ **Find and correct five errors in this paragraph.**

Check and Correct

- ❏ Circle two spelling errors and correct them.
- ❏ Underline two end punctuation errors and correct them.
- ❏ Correct one sentence fragment.

Student Model

> Being a forest ranger is hard. A big challenge. Why is this. First, they must know their reigon well. They must find lost campers? Also, forest rangers must warn campers about weather condishons. In addition, they have to be brave. If a bear attacks a camper, they have to catch it. In conclusion, forest rangers have a tough job.

Edit *Look at the sentences in your draft on page 25. Do they all have the correct end punctuation? Fix the ones that don't.*

Final Draft/Present

▶ **Write a final draft of your paragraph on paper or the computer. Check it again and correct any errors before you present it.**

Firefighter

Firefighters work in the city as well as in forests. Danita Thomas puts out fires in Syracuse, New York. When the alarm goes off at the firehouse, she and her crew race to the building in danger. Danita is always prepared to save families and buildings from the flames.

Name: Danita Thomas

Hometown: Syracuse, New York

Job: Firefighter

Duties:
- responds quickly to alarms
- uses equipment to put out fires
- works as part of a team
- rescues victims of fire

Skills:
- physical strength to hold hoses
- communicating with fire victims
- knowledge of fires
- working with other firefighters

Similar Jobs:
- Police Officer
- Emergency Medical Technician

Pay: $25,000 to $80,000

Education: High school diploma

It takes two people to control a powerful fire hose.

Danita is a firefighter and a mom. Here, she stands with her son Victor.

Ask Yourself

1. **Underline** Mark the skills you think you already have.

2. **Circle** Mark which duty would be hardest for you.

3. Would you want this job?

☐ Yes   ☐ Maybe   ☐ No

Using a Fire Evacuation Map

During a fire, Danita Thomas will enter buildings to save lives. If you are ever in a building during a fire drill or a real emergency, you'll need to leave the building. Large buildings have fire evacuation maps that tell you where to go. Look at the map below and answer the questions about it.

▶ **Fill in the circle next to the correct answer.**

1. Where is the meeting point?

Ⓐ on James Street
Ⓑ on Willow Street
Ⓒ on Main Street
Ⓓ in room 123

2. Which classrooms exit the building from the same door?

Ⓐ rooms 131 and 134
Ⓑ rooms 131 and 123
Ⓒ rooms 130 and 138
Ⓓ rooms 131 and 129

3. What do the arrows mean?

Ⓐ People should evacuate in that direction.
Ⓑ The fire will spread in that direction next.
Ⓒ That is where the firefighters should go.
Ⓓ That is the direction that car traffic goes.

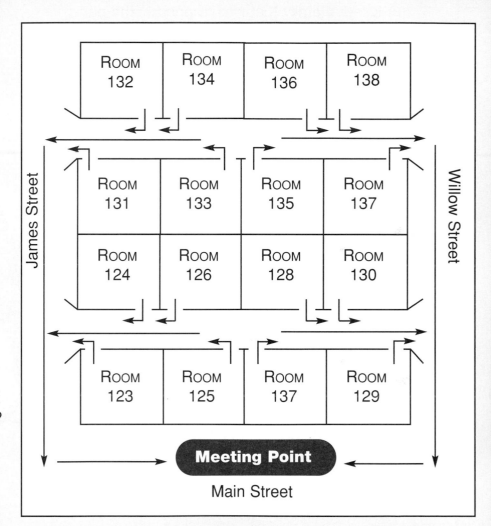

4. If you exit the building on James Street, what should you do next?

Ⓐ go straight for one block
Ⓑ turn left
Ⓒ go right
Ⓓ go back into the building

5. If you're not sure which way to go, what should you do?

Ⓐ walk out the nearest exit
Ⓑ look for an adult
Ⓒ look for a friend
Ⓓ wait for help

Comprehension

▶ **Fill in the circle next to the correct answer.**

1. The 1988 fire in Yellowstone National Park _____.

Ⓐ killed over 200 people

Ⓑ burned over 1.2 million acres

Ⓒ killed a family that was trapped in the park

Ⓓ made the park close down forever

Here's a Tip!
Read all of the answer choices before answering a question.

2. One way smoke jumpers fight fires is _____.

Ⓐ by using fire trucks

Ⓑ by calling 911

Ⓒ by digging ditches called "fire lines"

Ⓓ by reading books

3. What is the main idea of this Workshop?

Ⓐ Wildfires can't be stopped because they are out of control.

Ⓑ Firefighters are brave.

Ⓒ Every year in the U.S., firefighters must battle out-of-control wildfires.

Ⓓ Wildfires can be good for the environment.

4. What detail supports the idea that building homes in the foothills of California is dangerous?

Ⓐ Smoke jumpers are brave enough to jump into forest fires.

Ⓑ Fires need oxygen, fuel, and heat to burn.

Ⓒ California foothills are covered with brush that burns easily.

Ⓓ Fires can be put out with water.

5. What could someone do to protect a house during a wildfire?

Ⓐ Remove shrubs from around the house.

Ⓑ Stack firewood near the house.

Ⓒ Use a fan to change the wind's direction.

Ⓓ Remove all pets from the house.

Vocabulary

▶ **Fill in the circle next to the correct definitions of the underlined words.**

1. A thermometer shows the <u>degree</u> of temperature.
   - Ⓐ chill
   - Ⓒ a unit for measuring temperature
   - Ⓑ compass
   - Ⓓ an amount of something liquid

2. The fire <u>rapidly</u> approached the house.
   - Ⓐ easily
   - Ⓒ quickly
   - Ⓑ slowly
   - Ⓓ often

3. In <u>regions</u> of California, bushes and trees become <u>fuel</u> for spreading fires.
   - Ⓐ areas; something that can be burned
   - Ⓒ forests; tool
   - Ⓑ forests; something that can be stopped
   - Ⓓ governments; wind

▶ **Fill in the correct answer to the question.**

4. What is the meaning of the prefix in the word <u>rebuild</u>?
   - Ⓐ not
   - Ⓒ extra
   - Ⓑ again
   - Ⓓ undo

▶ **Fill in the word that best completes the sentence.**

5. The smoke jumper was a _____ of the wildfire.
   - Ⓐ survive
   - Ⓒ survivor
   - Ⓑ resurvive
   - Ⓓ surviving

Short Answer

▶ **Use what you've read in this Workshop to answer the question below. Check your spelling and grammar.**

What should you do if a wildfire approaches your home?

_____

_____

_____

_____

Workshop 2
Nonfiction

Comprehension Focus
Sequence of Events

READINGS
1 New to the U.S. >> Profile
2 My Journey to America >> Personal Narrative
3 A Nation of Immigrants >> Social Studies Text

Coming to AMERICA

Welcome to America! Many people hear those words when they arrive in the U.S. In fact, since this country was founded, over 55 million people have moved here from other nations.

Why do people take long, difficult journeys to make a new home in the U.S.? What's it like for a kid to move to America? Find out in this Workshop.

VOCABULARY BUILDER

Target Word ► Read the Target Words. Rate each one using the scale below.*	Meaning ► Read the Target Word meanings. Write in the missing ones.	Example ► Finish the Target Word examples below. Write in the missing ones.
achieve a•chieve (verb) ① ② ③		This year, I want to achieve . . .
globe globe (noun) ① ② ③	the world; a round object	
liberty li•ber•ty (noun) ① ② ③		On July 4, we celebrate our nation's **liberty** from England! 
route route (noun) ① ② ③	a way to get somewhere	
voyage voy•age (noun) ① ② ③		I'd like to take a voyage to . . .

*Rating Scale
① = I don't know it at all.
② = I've seen it before.
③ = I know it and use it.

The Big Idea

Write What is this article mainly about?

_____

_____

_____

VOCABULARY BUILDER

Target Word

translate

trans•late (verb)

Rate it: ① ② ③

Meaning

_____

_____

Example

_____

_____

_____

React

If you could live anywhere in the world, where would it be? Explain your choice.

New to the U.S.

The U.S. was a whole new world for Jair. Find out how he made himself at home.

September, 2005—It's hard moving to a new country—especially for a kid. Three years ago, Jair Saenz and his family moved from Peru, a country in South America. They settled in Akron, Pennsylvania.

At first, Jair didn't like his new home. He couldn't understand English. He couldn't speak to his classmates. He felt all alone.

Then, Jair made friends with a student who spoke Spanish. Jair's friend **translated** sentences for him. Jair also enrolled in a special class to learn English.

Next, Jair joined the soccer team. He had loved to play soccer in Peru. Playing in the U.S. helped him learn English rapidly. Jair and his teammates shouted directions to each other as they passed the ball. Soon, his new teammates were his new friends.

Now, Jair feels at home in America. He has achieved his goal of learning English. He has friends. And on the soccer field, he hears a familiar sound from home: The roar of the crowd when he scores a goal! **END**

Jair plays soccer with a friend.

Words to Know! **enrolled** signed up for

Sequence of Events

Sequence is the order in which events happen.
To find a sequence of events:

- Try to remember the order in which events take place.
- Look for times, dates, and signal words, such as *first*, *then*, *next*, *after*, and *finally*.
- When you know the order, check it again. Make sure it makes sense.

▶ **Fill in this chart with the sequence of events that tell about Jair's new life in the U.S.**

At first

Jair didn't like his new home.

Then

Next

Now

The Big Idea

Write What is this article mainly about?

_____

_____

_____

VOCABULARY BUILDER

 Target Word

journey
jour•ney *(noun)*

Rate it: ①   ②   ③

Meaning

_____

_____

Example

_____

_____

_____

 React

Virpal and her sister traveled alone for 13 hours. Would you be afraid to do that? Why or why not?

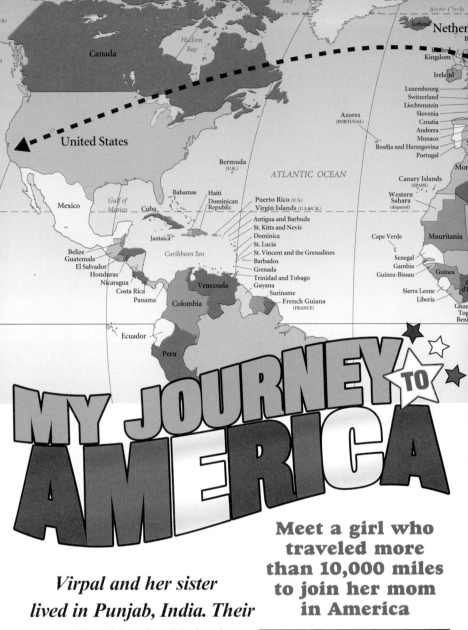

MY JOURNEY TO AMERICA

Meet a girl who traveled more than 10,000 miles to join her mom in America

Virpal and her sister lived in Punjab, India. Their mom lived in the United States. After five years apart, the girls took a voyage to reach their mother. The **journey** to America wasn't easy. This is Virpal's story in her own words.

Left Behind

My name is Virpal. I am 13 years old. I come from Punjab, India. Five years ago, my mom was granted a visa to move to America. My sister and I stayed behind in India. We lived with other family members. Not a day went by that I didn't dream about being back together with my mother. After five

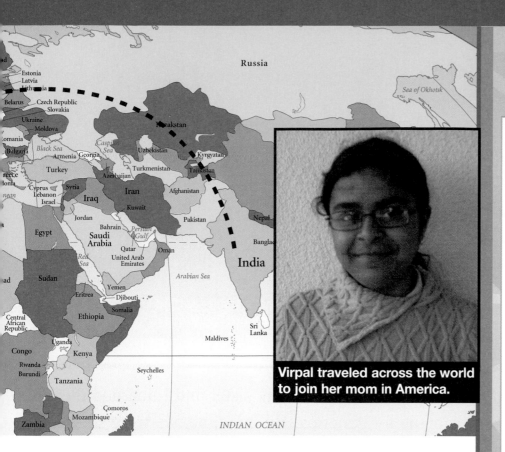

Virpal traveled across the world to join her mom in America.

1. **Write** Finish the sentences below to tell about two events from "Left Behind."

• Five years ago, Virpal's mother

_____

_____

_____

• After five years, _____

_____

_____

_____

2. **Underline** What did Virpal do after she was stopped by an airport worker?

years, the United States granted my sister and me permission to come live with our mother again.

On Our Way

Our trip across the globe started in Delhi, India. We made several stops along the route. First, we flew on a plane to Holland. There, we had to board another airplane. But that plane was delayed for four hours. My sister and I were hungry and thirsty. And we didn't have any money.

That wasn't our only problem. Next, an airport guard pulled me aside. He wanted to investigate a box that I was carrying. It was pretty obvious that my sister and I were from a different country. Luckily, while living in India, I took English classes. The airport worker understood some English, too. So, I was able to speak with him. I told him that the box was filled with sweets for my mother. ➡

Words to Know! **delayed** made late

Active Reading

 Underline Who helped Virpal find her mother?

VOCABULARY BUILDER

Target Word

familiar
fa•mil•iar *(adjective)*

Rate it: ① ② ③

Meaning

_____

_____

Example

_____

_____

_____

React

Write Do you think Virpal will continue to be happy in America? Or do you think she will want to go back to India?

_____

_____

_____

Virpal's family settled in Fresno, California.

Almost There

Four hours later, my sister and I boarded the plane for America. By this time, we were so tired and hungry that we were crying on the plane.

When we landed at the Los Angeles airport, I was so happy! But as soon as we got off the airplane, we were told to get in a long line. It felt like the longest wait ever. My sister and I began to worry. We were afraid our mother might think we didn't make it. We thought she might leave the airport before our reunion. Finally, an officer from the airport helped us find her. At last, our voyage was over.

Together at Last

That day was the happiest day of my life. Finally, I saw my mother again! It was great to see her **familiar** face. Today, I am a 7th-grade student in Fresno, California. I am in Mrs. Tracy's class, and I'm achieving my goal of reading and writing in English. I am also learning to love my new country. I didn't know America would be so beautiful! END

Words to Know! | **reunion** a meeting or gathering

Sequence of Events

▶ Fill in four important events from Virpal's journey to America. You'll find them in the sections "On Our Way" and "Almost There."

First

_____

_____

_____

Next

_____

_____

Four hours later

_____

_____

Finally

_____

_____

A NATION of IMMIGRANTS

Where do Americans come from? They come from all over the world!

The Big Idea

Write ▸ What is this article mainly about?

_____

_____

_____

VOCABULARY BUILDER

 Target Word

seek

seek (verb)

Rate it: ① ② ③

Meaning

_____

_____

Example

_____

_____

_____

React

Are there new immigrants in your community? Where are they from?

The First Americans

An immigrant is someone who moves from one country to another. The United States is a nation of immigrants! Throughout history, more than 55 million people have made the journey to America. And new immigrants are still coming today. They want good jobs. They want a better education. They are also **seeking** liberty.

The first people to live in America were Native Americans. They lived here for thousands of years. Then, in the 1500s and 1600s, European explorers came. They were English, French, Spanish, and Dutch. They built cities like New York and Boston.

During this time, millions of Africans also came to America. They were brought to the United States against their will—as slaves.

New Arrivals

The first major wave of immigration happened from 1845–1855. Nearly 11 million immigrants moved to America. One-and-a-half million came from Ireland. That country was suffering from a famine. More than one million others came from Germany. They were fleeing a war.

The next great wave of immigration lasted from 1891–1901. Millions of Asians, Italians, Greeks, Jews, and Slavs moved to the U.S.

Today, there are 33 million immigrants living in the U.S. From 1981–1990 more than eight million immigrants arrived! Over half were from Central and South America and Mexico. But they were not the first Spanish-speaking people to come here. ➡

This immigrant family arrived in the United States in the 1890s.

Words to Know!   **famine**   a serious lack of food

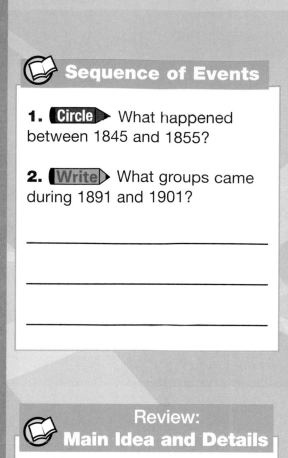

Sequence of Events

1. [Circle] What happened between 1845 and 1855?

2. [Write] What groups came during 1891 and 1901?

_____

_____

_____

Review: Main Idea and Details

1. [Circle] Find the main idea in the section, "The First Americans."

2. [Underline] Find one important detail that supports the main idea.

Active Reading

Underline ▶ Which states did many Mexicans move to in the 1700s and 1800s?

VOCABULARY BUILDER
◎ Target Word

culture

cul•ture (noun)

Rate it: ① ② ③

Meaning

_____

_____

Example

_____

_____

_____

React

Write ▶ Imagine moving to another country. What would you miss most about America?

_____

_____

_____

_____

History of Hispanic Immigration

Spanish settlers first came to the United States almost 450 years ago. In 1565, Pedro Menéndez de Avilés, a Spanish explorer, founded the city of St. Augustine in Florida. It is the oldest city in the United States. In 1598, Spanish settlers arrived in New Mexico. There, they established the capital city of Santa Fe.

During the 1700s and 1800s, Hispanic immigration continued. Mexicans moved to Texas, Arizona, and California. By 1900, the Mexican-American population was more than 400,000.

After that, the mid-1900s saw the next big group of Hispanic immigrants. During this time, large numbers of Puerto Ricans moved to the U.S. mainland. In the 1960s, there was political unrest in Cuba. Cuban immigration to the U.S. rose. By the 1980s, Hispanics accounted for more than one-third of all U.S. immigrants.

TEXT FEATURE Reading a Circle Graph

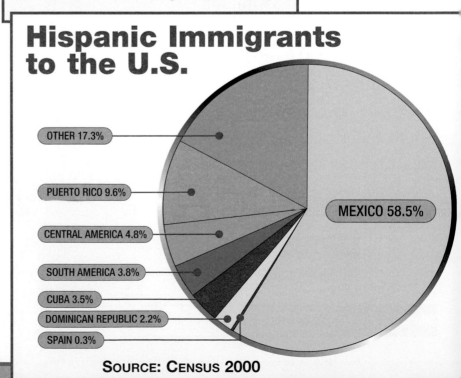

Hispanic Immigrants to the U.S.

- OTHER 17.3%
- PUERTO RICO 9.6%
- CENTRAL AMERICA 4.8%
- SOUTH AMERICA 3.8%
- CUBA 3.5%
- DOMINICAN REPUBLIC 2.2%
- SPAIN 0.3%
- MEXICO 58.5%

SOURCE: CENSUS 2000

The American flag is a symbol of pride in our country.

Immigration Today

Today, Hispanic-Americans are the fastest-growing minority group in the United States. They come from many different countries and **cultures**. Immigrants from Asia are also arriving in large numbers. They come from countries such as China, Vietnam, Laos, and Thailand.

All immigrants leave something behind—family, a home, a way of life. But they also bring things with them. New foods, music, and traditions from around the world change our country every year. END

| Words to Know! | **establish** to found or start something |

A circle graph shows percentages of a whole.

1. From which country do most Hispanic immigrants come?

Ⓐ Mexico   Ⓒ Dominican Republic
Ⓑ Cuba   Ⓓ Puerto Rico

2. From which country do 2.2% of Hispanic immigrants come?

Ⓐ Mexico   Ⓒ Dominican Republic
Ⓑ Cuba   Ⓓ Puerto Rico

3. What is the source of information for this graph?

_____

_____

Sequence of Events

1. Underline ▷ When did the first Spanish immigrants come to America?

2. Write ▷ When did Hispanics become more than a third of all U.S. immigrants?

_____

_____

_____

_____

Skills Check

1. Write ▷ What happened around 1960?

_____

_____

2. Write ▷ Number these events in the correct sequence from 1 to 3.

_____ The Mexican-American population was more than 400,000.

_____ St. Augustine was founded.

_____ Cubans came to the U.S.

Take the WORD CHALLENGE

★ START

1 Rate them. How familiar are these foods to you?
1 = not familiar at all
2 = tried it once or twice
3 = very familiar

____ french fries

____ pad thai

____ meatloaf

____ burrito

2 Rate them. Rate the following journeys.
1 = most interesting
4 = least interesting

____ taking a cross-country train ride

____ hiking to the top of a mountain

____ visiting another country

____ going to a park to visit a friend

3 Synonyms
Synonyms are words that have similar meanings. Examples are *fast* and *quick* or *pretty* and *beautiful*.

Draw a line from each word below to its synonym.

journey   find

region   voyage

locate   area

liberty   freedom

This game is **great**!

This game is **awesome**!

You two always say the same thing about every game.

4 Fill in. Name one item you might **seek** in each of these places.

a pet store _____

a music store _____

a sports store _____

a clothing store _____

5 Fill in. Finish the sentences below by writing these words in the blanks: route, seek, globe.

Hundreds of years ago, sailors decided to _____

a path around the world. Magellan was the first explorer to

find such a _____. It took him and his crew

3 years to sail around the _____! They finished

their journey in 1522.

6 Write it. Translate each of these terms or symbols into an English word or phrase.

:) means: _____
_____

means: _____
_____

means: _____
_____

C U L8R means: _____
_____

---

7 Choose and Explain.
If you could take a voyage anywhere in the world:

Where would you go?

_____

Why?

_____

_____

Who would you like to go with?

_____

8 Antonyms
Antonyms are words that have opposite meanings. Examples are *good* and *bad* or *miserable* and *happy*.

Draw a line from each word below to its antonym.

familiar	destroy
rebuild	strange
seek	avoid

A Chihuahua is a **tiny** dog. A Great Dane is a **huge** dog.

9 Match them. Match each food on the left with the culture it comes from on the right.

burrito	Japanese
egg roll	Chinese
pizza	Mexican
sushi	Italian

10 Check them. Which two goals would you most like to achieve?

☐ saving enough money for a new MP3 player

☐ getting good grades on your next report card

☐ improving your score on your favorite video game

☐ winning a spot on a TV game show

☐ learning to play a musical instrument

FINISH

Writing Focus
Narrative Paragraph

A narrative paragraph tells a story about an event.

▶ **Check out Eric's narrative paragraph about a trip to the Statue of Liberty.**

Student Model

> My Best Field Trip Ever
>
> by Eric Washington
>
> Last year, my class took a trip to the Statue of Liberty. First, we set out on our journey by boat. Then, the Statue of Liberty came into view. She was as tall as a building. Her familiar face was huge! Next, we landed at Liberty Island. We climbed up to the top of the base and saw the copper insides of the statue. It was cool to be so close to a symbol of freedom. Finally, the boat came back to Manhattan. It was the best field trip I've ever been on!

Parts of a Narrative Paragraph

▶ **Find these parts of Eric's narrative paragraph.**

1. Underline the sentence that tells about the **experience**.
2. Put a check beside three **details** that explain the experience.
3. Number three details in the **order** they happened.
4. Circle the **linking words** that connect the details.
5. Put a star beside the sentence that **sums up** the event and tells the writer's feelings about the experience.

Brainstorm

▶ Read the writing prompt in the middle of the web. Then, use the questions to help you brainstorm your ideas.

Class Trips

Writing Prompt:
Tell what happened on a fun trip you've taken.

Trips With Family

Trips With Friends

Narrative Paragraph | **Plan**

Plan Your Paragraph

Writing Prompt: Tell what happened on a fun trip you've taken.

▶ **Use this chart to plan and organize your paragraph.**

Word Choices

_____

_____

_____

_____

_____

Event

- *Last year, . . .*
- *Once when I was . . .*
- *The best trip ever was . . .*

First Detail

- *First, . . .*
- *It began with . . .*
- *At the start . . .*

Second Detail

- *Then, . . .*
- *After that, . . .*
- *Next, . . .*

Third Detail

- *Next, . . .*
- *Suddenly, . . .*
- *The next thing we did was . . .*

Ending

- *Finally, . . .*
- *In the end, . . .*
- *Once it was over, . . .*

Write a First Draft

▶ **Use the writing frame to write a first draft of your paragraph.**

_____

(title)

Last year, _____

_____

_____

First, _____

_____

_____

Then, _____

_____

_____

_____

Next, _____

_____

_____

_____

Finally, _____

_____

_____

_____

Revise

▶ **Rate your paragraph. Then have a writing partner rate it.**

Scoring Guide			
weak	okay	good	strong
1	2	3	4

1. Does the beginning tell about the **experience**?

Self	1	2	3	4
Partner	1	2	3	4

2. Are there **details** that explain the experience?

Self	1	2	3	4
Partner	1	2	3	4

3. Are the details written in the **order** they happened?

Self	1	2	3	4
Partner	1	2	3	4

4. Do **linking words** connect the details?

Self	1	2	3	4
Partner	1	2	3	4

5. Does the ending **sum up** the event and tell the writer's feelings about it?

Self	1	2	3	4
Partner	1	2	3	4

▶ **Now revise your paragraph to make it stronger.**

Grammar CORRECTING SENTENCE FRAGMENTS

A **sentence fragment** is an incomplete sentence. Often, sentence fragments are missing a subject or a verb. To fix some fragments, add a subject or verb to make a **complete sentence**.

Example

Sentence Fragment	Complete Sentence
Settlers from Europe. [missing verb] Moved to America. [missing subject]	Settlers came from Europe. Settlers moved to America.

▶ **Write whether each fragment below is missing a subject or a verb.**

1. couldn't talk to other kids   *subject*

2. met a friend who spoke Spanish   _____

3. at first, life in Akron   _____

4. then, shouted instructions to his team   _____

5. Jair and his friends   _____

To correct some **sentence fragments**, you can connect the fragment to a complete sentence by adding a comma and any missing words.

Example

Sentence and Fragment	Complete Sentence
Virpal's mom lived in the United States. Her grandma in India. [missing verb]	Virpal's mom lived in the United States, and her grandma lived in India.

▶ **Rewrite each sentence and fragment as one complete sentence.**

6. The family came together again. But not easy.

   _____

7. Their plane was delayed. Waited for four hours.

   _____

8. Finally, the sisters saw their mother. Hugged them both.

   _____

9. Virpal thinks America is beautiful. Happy to be here.

   _____

 Edit *Take a close look at each of the sentences in your draft on page 49. Are any of them sentence fragments? Fix the ones that are.*

Mechanics USING CAPITALS

Some words begin with a **capital letter**.

- The first word in a sentence begins with a capital letter.
- A proper noun begins with a capital letter.

Example

Correct	Incorrect
The girls were all alone.	the girls were all alone.
The guard asked Virpal to stop.	The guard asked virpal to stop.

▶ **Find and correct five errors in this paragraph.**

Student Model

> Once, when I was ten, my family visited San Francisco. At first, I was afraid to fly. Then, I calmed down. Had fun on the plane. Soon, we were walking around the most beautiful city! I really liked the big hills and streetcars. Next, we visited Chinatown. my mother spoke chinese to the waiter. She tranlated the menu for us. In the end, it was a great journy for the whole family!

Check and Correct

- ☐ Circle two spelling errors and correct them.
- ☐ Underline two capitalization errors and correct them.
- ☐ Correct one sentence fragment.

 Edit *Look at the sentences in your draft on page 49. Do they all use capitals correctly? Fix the ones that don't.*

Final Draft/Present

▶ **Write a final draft of your paragraph on paper or the computer. Check it again and correct any errors before you present it.**

Careers

Airport Security Worker

Have you ever been on a plane? Maybe you remember being "screened" before you could fly. "Screening" is when you walk through a metal detector, or have your bags X-rayed. The people helping you do this are called screeners. Craig Martelle is a screener in Pittsburgh. "Dealing with the public and making them safer feels good," he said.

Name: Craig Martelle

Hometown: Pittsburgh, Pennsylvania

Job: Screener at Pittsburgh International Airport

Duties:
- checks for firearms, explosives, or other forbidden items
- assists passengers in finding their flights and getting to their gates on time

Skills:
- ability to operate an X-ray machine
- communication skills
- the ability to lift at least 40 lb.

Similar Jobs:
- Store detective
- Security guard

Pay: $12.50 per hour

Education: High school diploma

Screeners like Craig work hard to make flying safe.

Ask Yourself

1. **Underline** ▷ Mark the level of education needed for this job.

2. Would you like working with different people all day? Why or why not?

_____

_____

_____

3. Would you want this job?

☐ Yes ☐ Maybe ☐ No

Reading Flight Schedules

If a flight is about to leave, Craig makes sure that passengers will get through security on time. He must monitor the flight schedules while he works. Passengers must use flight schedules as well. Look at the flight schedules below. Then answer the questions.

ARRIVALS

Arriving from	Airline	Flight #	Gate	Time	Baggage	Remarks
Lima, Peru	South American	1681	A23	12:15 P.M.	B	arrived
London, England	England Airlines	4704	B40	12:30 P.M.	A	arrived

DEPARTURES

Departing to	Airline	Flight #	Gate	Time	Remarks
Cancun, Mexico	Mexican Travels	1240	F9	11:45 A.M.	delayed 2 hours
Shanghai, China	Asian Pacific	130	D77	12:45 P.M.	canceled

▶ **Fill in the circle next to the correct answer.**

1. At which gate will flight 4704 from London arrive?

(A) gate A23

(B) gate B40

(C) gate 130

(D) gate 1707

2. At 1:00 P.M., where do you think the best place is to find passengers from flight 4704?

(A) London

(B) baggage claim A

(C) baggage claim 1240

(D) baggage claim B

3. You are catching flight 130 to Shanghai. Where should you go?

(A) to gate A23

(B) to gate D77

(C) to baggage claim E

(D) Go to a customer service counter. Your flight's been canceled.

4. Which airline flies to and from Lima, Peru?

(A) England Airlines

(B) South American

(C) Asian Pacific

(D) Mexican Travels

5. It's 11:45 A.M. now. You are waiting for your plane to Cancun. Do you have time to buy a soda?

(A) No, the flight is about to take off.

(B) No, your plane is leaving in 15 minutes.

(C) Yes, the plane has been delayed two hours.

(D) No, you need to wait to find out the gate assignment.

Workshop Wrap-Up

Comprehension

▶ **Fill in the circle next to the correct answer.**

1. When Jair Saenz first moved to America, he couldn't understand the _____.

   Ⓐ temperature

   Ⓑ time

   Ⓒ language

   Ⓓ holidays

> **Here's a Tip!**
> For fill-in-the-blank questions, substitute each answer for the blank in the sentence. Then pick the best one.

2. Why did Virpal move to America?

   Ⓐ She was coming to be with her older sister.

   Ⓑ She was moving to be with her mother.

   Ⓒ She was moving to get away from her family.

   Ⓓ She wanted to learn a new language.

3. What happened to Virpal during her journey to the U.S.?

   Ⓐ She was stopped by a guard in a European airport.

   Ⓑ She was met by her mom in a European airport.

   Ⓒ She moved to Canada for five years.

   Ⓓ Her mom came to meet her in India.

4. How long have Spanish-speaking people been living in the United States?

   Ⓐ since 1970

   Ⓑ since 1565

   Ⓒ since 1995

   Ⓓ since the beginning of time

5. What is the fastest growing group of immigrants in the United States?

   Ⓐ Hispanics

   Ⓑ Italians

   Ⓒ Australians

   Ⓓ French

Vocabulary

▶ **Fill in the circle next to the correct definition of the underlined word.**

1. China is on the other side of the <u>globe</u> from the United States.
   - Ⓐ country
   - Ⓒ society
   - Ⓑ attitude
   - Ⓓ world

2. Americans have the <u>liberty</u> to voice their opinions.
   - Ⓐ freedom
   - Ⓒ slavery
   - Ⓑ money
   - Ⓓ knowledge

3. Do you know the fastest <u>route</u> to school from your home?
   - Ⓐ car
   - Ⓒ way to get somewhere
   - Ⓑ bus line
   - Ⓓ time on a clock

▶ **Choose the antonym for the underlined word.**

4. The scientist <u>achieved</u> his goal of finding a cure for the disease.
   - Ⓐ won
   - Ⓒ failed
   - Ⓑ accomplished
   - Ⓓ found

▶ **Choose the synonym for the underlined word.**

5. Virpal's <u>voyage</u> from India to the United States was very long.
   - Ⓐ airplane
   - Ⓒ trip
   - Ⓑ luggage
   - Ⓓ walk

Short Answer

▶ **Use what you've learned in this Workshop to answer the question below. Check your spelling and grammar.**

If you were new to America, what would be the most difficult thing for you to get used to? Why?

_____

_____

_____

Workshop ③
Literature

Comprehension Focus
Story Elements

READING
Bud's Breakfast >> Historical Fiction

BUD, NOT BUDDY

Christopher Paul Curtis had a big secret. He was working in a car factory. But he really wanted to be a writer. He started working on a book. Finally, he finished it. Kids loved it.

Now, Curtis writes full time. "If I knew writing was this much fun," he says. "I would have started when I was four."

Curtis's second book is *Bud, Not Buddy*. Bud is a young boy on his own. He's looking for his father. Often he's poor and hungry. Bud's sense of humor gets him through a lot of hard times. But now and then he needs a little extra help.

VOCABULARY BUILDER

◎ Target Word ▶ Read the Target Words. Rate each one using the scale below.*	Meaning ▶ Read the Target Word meanings. Write in the missing ones.	Example ▶ Finish the Target Word examples below. Write in the missing ones.
available a•vail•a•ble (adjective) ① ② ③		When free time is available, I like to . . .
grateful grate•ful (adjective) ① ② ③	thankful	
improve im•prove (verb) ① ② ③		If I practice, my skateboarding skills will **improve**.
patient pa•tient (adjective) ① ② ③	able to wait calmly for a long time	
privilege priv•i•lege (noun) ① ② ③		Some privileges we get in school are . . .

*Rating Scale
① = I don't know it at all.
② = I've seen it before.
③ = I know it and use it.

Comprehension Focus
Story Elements

A **novel** is a book that tells a story about made-up characters and events. "Bud's Breakfast" is a part of the novel *Bud, Not Buddy*. The novel is historical fiction, which means it is set in the past. To understand a story, look for these elements:

1. **Setting** is where and when a story takes place. This story takes place in Flint, Michigan, during the Great Depression of the 1930s. It was a time when many people were poor and hungry.

2. **Characters** are the people in the story. The main character is the most important character. These are the main characters in this story:

Bud,
a 10-year-old boy

the man at the mission

Bud's pretend family

3. **Plot** is the sequence of events in a story. The plot contains a problem that the main character needs to solve. In "Bud's Breakfast," Bud is living on his own. He needs to eat. But when he gets turned away from the food line at the mission, he's got a big problem. Will Bud go hungry?

▶ **Turn the page to begin reading Bud's story.**

BUD'S BREAKFAST

▶ Fill in this chart as you reread the story.

	Part 1 (pp. 60–63)	Part 2 (pp. 64–67)	Part 3 (pp. 68–71)
Setting	Time: one morning in the 1930s Place: Flint, Michigan	Time: Place:	Time: Place:
Character	Who is the main character? Describe him/her:	How does the character change?	What is the character like now?
Plot Events	What happens at the beginning of the story?	What happens in the middle of the story?	How does the story end?

Active Reading

Star What does the man at the mission tell Bud?

VOCABULARY BUILDER
Target Word

farther
far•ther (adverb)

Rate it: ① ② ③

Meaning

_____
_____

Example

_____
_____
_____

React

Bud is hungry. But the man at the mission turns him away. What would you do if you were Bud?

Bud's Breakfast
by Christopher Paul Curtis

UH-OH. My eyes opened and I could see the sun behind the branch of a Christmas tree.

I jumped up, folded my blanket inside my suitcase, hid it, and started running the six or seven blocks down to the mission.

I turned the corner and said, "Whew!" There were still people lined up waiting. I started walking along the line. The end was a lot **farther** away than

Words to Know! **mission** a church or other place where aid is given to people in need

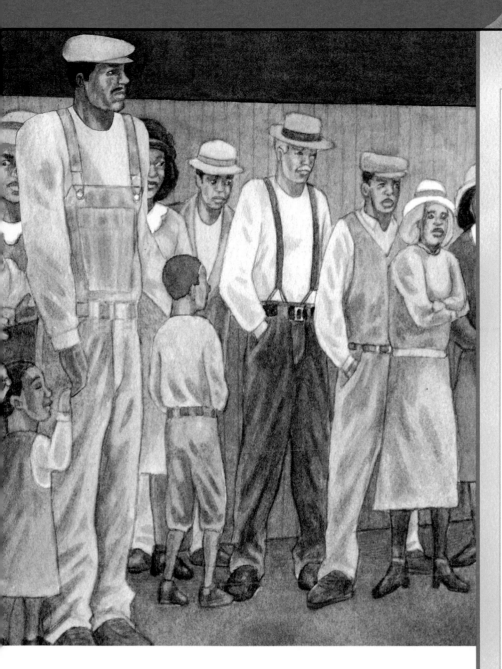

Story Elements

Setting

1. **Circle** ▶ As the story begins, Bud has been sleeping outside. Find a detail that helps you know this.

Character

2. **Write** ▶ How do you think Bud feels right now?

_____

_____

_____

_____

Plot

3. **Write** ▶ What problem does Bud have?

_____

_____

_____

_____

_____

I thought. The line turned all the way around two corners, then crossed over one street before I saw the last person. Shucks. I walked up to get behind him.

He said, "Line's closed. These here folks are the last ones." He pointed at a man standing next to a woman who was carrying a baby.

I said, "But sir . . ."

He said, "But nothing. Line's closed. These here folks are the last ones." ➡

Active Reading

Star ▶ What does the man take out of his pocket?

VOCABULARY BUILDER

 Target Word

expect

ex•pect (verb)

Rate it: ① ② ③

Meaning

_____

_____

Example

_____

_____

_____

_____

React

Someone is putting his hand on Bud's neck. What might Bud be thinking?

It was time to start lying. If I didn't get any food now I'd have to steal something out of someone's garbage. Or I wouldn't be able to eat until the mission opened for supper.

I said, "Sir, I—"

The man raised his hand and said, "Look, kid, everybody's got a story. And everybody knows the rules. The line closes at seven o'clock. How's it fair to these people who been here since five o'clock that you can sleep until"—he looked at his wristwatch—"until seven-fifteen? Then you come busting down here **expecting** to eat? You think you got some kind of special privilege just 'cause you're skinny and raggedy? Look in the line. There's lots of folks look just like you. You ain't the worst."

"Supper starts at six P.M., but you see how things is. If you plan on getting fed you better be in line by four. Now get out of here before I get rough with you."

Shucks, being hungry for a whole day is about as bad at it can get. I said, "But . . ."

He reached in his pocket and pulled something out that looked like a heavy black strap. He slapped it across his hand. Uh-oh, here we go again.

He said, "That's it, no more talk. You opened your mouth one time too many. You rotten kids today don't listen to no one. But I'ma show you something that'll improve your hearing." He slapped the strap on his hand and started walking toward me.

Words to Know! **raggedy** torn and in bad condition

I was wrong when I said being hungry for a day is about as bad as it can get. Being hungry plus having a big knot on your head from a black leather strap would be even worse.

I backed away. But I only got two steps before I felt a giant warm hand wrap around my neck from behind. I looked up to see who's doggone hand was so doggone big and why they'd put it around my neck. →

Story Elements

Setting

1. **Circle** ▶ What time does the breakfast line at the mission close? What time does Bud arrive?

Character

2. **Underline** ▶ Find two words that describe Bud.

Plot

3. **Write** ▶ Does it seem like Bud's problem is getting better or worse? Explain.

_____

_____

_____

_____

_____

Now go to page 59. Add details to Part 1 of the chart.

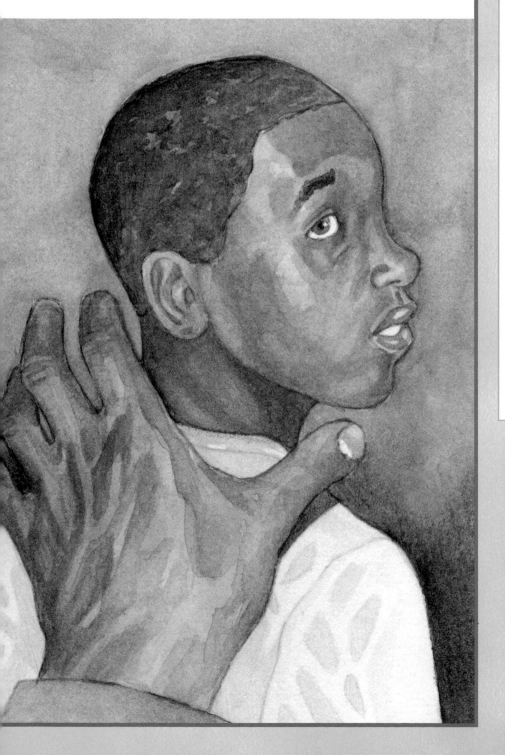

Active Reading

Star ▶ What name does the man call Bud?

React

Write ▶ If you were Bud, would you trust this family? Why or why not?

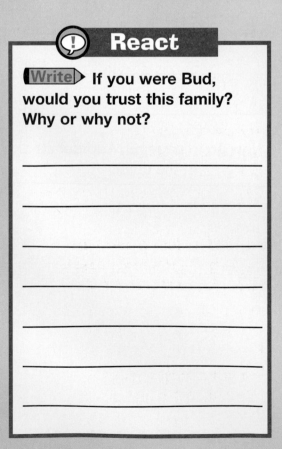

_____

_____

_____

_____

_____

_____

A very tall, square-shaped man in old blue overalls looked down at me. He said, "Clarence, what took you so long?"

I got ready to say, "My name's not Clarence. And please don't choke me, sir. I'll leave." But as soon as I opened my mouth he gave my head a shake. He said, "I told you to hurry back, now where you been?" He gave me a shove and said, "Get back in line with your momma."

Setting
1. **Write** Where does Bud join his pretend family?

_____

_____

_____

Character
2. **Underline** What does the man who pretends to be Bud's father order him to do?

Plot
3. **Write** What happens in this part of the story?

_____

_____

_____

_____

_____

_____

I looked up and down the line to see who was supposed to be my momma. Then a woman pointed her finger at her feet and said, "Clarence, you get over here right now." There were two little kids hanging on to her skirt.

I walked over to where she was. And she gave me a good hard smack on the head. Shucks, for someone who was just pretending to be my momma she sure did slap me a good one. ➡

Literature

Active Reading

Write ▶ What do the people in line think when Bud cuts in front of them?

_____

_____

_____

VOCABULARY BUILDER

◎ Target Word

gigantic

gi•gan•tic (adjective)

Rate it: ① ② ③

Meaning

_____

_____

Example

_____

_____

_____

❗ React

If you were poor and hungry, what would you think of the sign hanging over the mission?

I said, "Ow!"

The big square man who'd grabbed my neck looked at the man with the strap. He said, "Boy had to go use the crapper. Told him not to waste time. But like you said, these kids today don't listen to nobody."

The strap man looked at the size of the man who called me Clarence. Then he walked back to the end of the line.

When the overall man got back in line I said, "Thank you, sir, I really tried to get—" But _he_ popped me in the back of the head, hard, and said, "Next time don't be gone so long."

The two little kids busted out laughing and said, "Nyah-nyah-nyah-nyah-nyah, Clarence got a lickin', Clarence got a lickin'."

I told them, "Shut up, and don't call me—" Then _both_ my pretend poppa and my pretend momma smacked my head.

She looked at the people directly behind us and said, "Mercy, when they get to be this age . . ."

The people weren't too happy about me taking cuts in the line. But when they looked at how big my pretend daddy was and they saw how hard him and my pretend momma were going upside my head they decided they wouldn't say anything.

I was grateful to these people. But I wished they'd quit popping me in the head. And it seems like with all the names in the world they could've come up with a better one for me than Clarence.

I stood in line with my pretend family for a long, long time. Everybody was very quiet about standing in line, even my pretend brother and sister and all the other kids. When we finally got around the last corner and could see the door and folks

going in, it seemed like a bubble busted. People started laughing and talking. The main thing people were talking about was the great big sign that was hanging over the building.

It showed a **gigantic** picture of a family of four rich white people sitting in a car and driving somewhere. You could tell it was a family 'cause they all looked exactly alike. The only difference amongst them was that the daddy had a big head and a hat. The momma had the same head with a woman's hat. The girl had two big yellow pigtails coming out from above her ears. They all had big shiny teeth and big shiny eyes and big shiny cheeks and big shiny smiles. Shucks, you'd need to squint your eyes if that shiny family drove anywhere near you.

You could tell they were rich 'cause the car looked like it had room for eight or nine more people in it. They had movie star clothes on. The woman was wearing a coat with a hunk of fur around the neck. The man was wearing a suit and a tie. And the kids looked like they were wearing ten-dollar-apiece jackets.

Writ about their car in fancy letters it said, THERE'S NO PLACE LIKE AMERICA TODAY!

My pretend daddy read it and said, "Uh-uh-uh, well, you got to give them credit. You wouldn't expect that they'd have the nerve to come down here and tell the truth." ➡

Words to Know!	**nerve** courage

Story Elements

Setting
1. **Circle** What do the people in line see that they talk about?

Character
2. **Write** How do you think Bud feels in this part of the story?

_____

_____

_____

_____

_____

Plot
3. **Write** How is the pretend family helping Bud with his problem?

_____

_____

_____

_____

_____

_____

Now go to page 59. Add details to Part 2 of the chart.

Literature

 Active Reading

Write What does the mission serve for breakfast?

_____

_____

_____

VOCABULARY BUILDER

 Target Word

worth
worth (adjective)

Rate it: ① ② ③

Meaning

_____

_____

Example

_____

_____

_____

 React

What does this part of the story tell you about how hungry people were during the Great Depression?

When we finally got into the building it was **worth** the wait. The first thing you noticed when you got inside was how big the place was, and how many people were in it and how quiet it was. The only sound you could hear was when someone scraped a spoon across the bottom of their bowl or pulled a chair in or put one back. Or when the people in front of you dragged their feet on the floor moving up to where they were spooning out the food.

Words to Know! **scraped** scratched

Story Elements

Setting
1. **Circle** ▶ How is the inside of the mission described?

Character
2. **Write** ▶ How does Bud look in the picture?

_____

Plot
3. **Write** ▶ How has Bud's problem been solved? Explain.

_____

_____

_____

_____

_____

Review: Read for Detail

Write ▶ What are the three kinds of sounds that Bud hears inside the mission?

1._____

_____

2._____

_____

3._____

_____

After we'd picked up our spoons and bowls a lady dug a big mess of oatmeal out of a giant pot. She swopped it down into our bowls. She smiled and said, "I hope you enjoy."

Me and my pretend family all said, "Thank you, ma'am." Then a man put two pieces of bread and an apple and a big glass of milk on your tray. He said, "Please read the signs to your children. Thank you." ➡

Literature

Active Reading

 Star What does Bud ask his pretend family after they finish eating?

VOCABULARY BUILDER

 Target Word

normally

nor•mal•ly (adverb)

Rate it: ① ② ③

Meaning

_____

_____

Example

_____

_____

_____

 React

Do you like Bud? Would you want to be his friend? Explain why or why not.

We all said, "Thank you, sir." Then we walked past some signs someone'd stuck up on the wall.

One said, PLEASE DO NOT SMOKE. Another said, PLEASE EAT AS QUICKLY AND QUIETLY AS POSSIBLE. Another one said, PLEASE BE CONSIDERATE AND PATIENT—CLEAN UP AFTER YOURSELF—YOUR NEIGHBORS WILL BE EATING AFTER YOU. And the last one said, WE ARE TERRIBLY SORRY BUT WE HAVE NO WORK AVAILABLE.

My pretend daddy read the signs to my pretend brother and sister. We all sat at a long table with strangers on both sides of us.

The oatmeal was delicious! I poured some of my milk into it so it wouldn't be so lumpy and mixed it all together.

My pretend mother opened her pocketbook. She took out a little brown envelope. She reached inside of it and sprinkled something on my pretend brother's and sister's oatmeal. Then she said to

them, "I know that's not as much as you **normally** get. But I wanted to ask you if you minded sharing some with Clarence."

They pouted and gave me a couple of dirty looks. My pretend mother said, "Good." She emptied the rest of the envelope over my oatmeal. Brown sugar!

Shucks, I didn't even mind them calling me Clarence anymore. I said, "Thank you, Momma, ma'am."

She and my pretend daddy laughed. And he said, "It took you long enough to catch on, Clarence." He acted like he was going to smack me again, but he didn't.

After we'd finished all our food, we put our bowls up. And I thanked my pretend family again. I asked them, "Are you going to be coming back for supper?"

My pretend momma said, "No, dear, we only come here mornings. But you make sure you get here plenty early, you hear?"

I said, "Yes, Momma, I mean, ma'am."

I watched them walking away. My pretend brother looked back at me and stuck out his tongue. Then he reached up and took my pretend mother's hand. I couldn't really blame him. I don't think I'd be real happy about sharing my brown sugar and my folks with any strange kids either. (END)

Words to Know! **considerate** thoughtful

Story Elements

Character

1. (Write) How does Bud feel about what his pretend brother does?

_____

_____

_____

Plot

2. (Write) How does the story end?

_____

_____

_____

_____

Now go to page 59. Complete Part 3 of the chart.

Skills Check

1. (Underline) What advice does the mother give to Bud?

2. (Write) How did the family help Bud?

_____

_____

_____

Take the WORD CHALLENGE

START

1 **Check it.** Which service below would you like to be available for free? Pick one.

☐ doctor visits

☐ Internet access

☐ bus and subway rides

~ ~ ~ ~ ~ ~ ~ ~

2 **Decide.** Which situations below would make you feel grateful. Write **Yes** or **No** beside each situation.

_____ You forget your lunch. Your friend shares his.

_____ You get new sneakers. Your brother wears them to paint his bedroom.

_____ Your friend breaks a window. She says you did it.

_____ Your bike gets a flat tire. Your sister patches it.

3 **Homophones**

Homophones are words that sound alike but have different meanings and spellings. Examples are *piece* and *peace* or *wait* and *weight*.

Match each word to its homophone below.

| bear | by | rode |

Homophone

buy: _____

road: _____

bare: _____

Doctors need to have a lot of **patience** with their **patients**.

Fill in the sentence with two homophones. (Hint: One is a color.)

The wind _____ my new _____ shirt right off the clothesline.

4 **Fill it in.** Fill in the blanks with expect or worth.

Playing the drums is really fun. Of course, you can't

_____ to be good right away. It takes a lot of

practice. But in the end, the hard work is _____ it.

~ ~ ~ ~ ~ ~ ~ ~ ~ ~ ~ ~

5 **Decide.** Read each choice. Write **P** if you consider it a privilege. Write **NP** if it's not a privilege for you.

_____ staying up late   _____ taking out the trash

_____ taking music lessons   _____ getting an allowance

_____ going to the movies   _____ starring in the class play

6 Check one. How would you improve your school?
Pick one or more.

☐ add books to the library

☐ serve better food in the lunchroom

☐ make the school day longer

Now, add your own idea:

_____

_____

7 Think about it. When do you find it hardest to be patient?
Rank these situations from 1 to 4.
1 = hardest to be patient
4 = easiest to be patient

_____ waiting in line to ride your favorite roller coaster

_____ waiting to open your birthday gifts

_____ waiting to get a shot at the doctor's office

_____ waiting for a pizza delivery

8 Word Families
A **word family** is a group of words that share the same base word and have related meanings, such as *normal*, *normally*, and *abnormal*. *Normal* means "usual" or "expected." *Normally* means "usually." *Abnormal* means "unusual" or "not normal."

Normally, I'm normal. But today I'm WEIRD!

Complete each sentence with *normal*, *normally*, or *abnormal*.

1. Carlos _____ doesn't sleep late, but today he slept until noon.

2. His _____ wake-up time is 7:00 A.M.

3. It is _____ for Carlos to sleep later than 7:00 A.M.

9 Rank them. You got picked to be on a new reality show. You know you'll have to eat something gross. Which of these things would be the toughest for you to eat? Rank them from 1 to 4.
1 = not so tough   4 = really tough

_____ a gigantic jar of mustard

_____ a gigantic spider

_____ a gigantic bowl of worms

_____ a gigantic piece of raw fish.

10 Circle it. Which is farther away from where you live?

your school **OR** the nearest park

the grocery store **OR** the post office

the movie theater **OR** your best friend's house

FINISH

Literature Response | Model

Writing Focus
Literature Response

In a **literature response**, a reader relates a piece of literature to his or her life.

▶ **Read Megan's literature response to "Bud's Breakfast."**

Student Model

My Response to "Bud's Breakfast"
by Megan Richards

Like Bud, I have been helped by a stranger. It all started when I was shopping with my mom. I stopped to look at a pair of earrings. My mom kept walking farther away. She didn't know I had stopped. After that, I didn't know where my mom was. A store employee was nearby. I told her that I was lost. She took me to the front of the store and made an announcement over the store's loudspeaker. She patiently stayed with me. Finally, my mom came. I felt like Bud did. I was very grateful for help from a kind stranger.

Parts of a Literature Response

▶ **Find these parts of Megan's literature response.**

1. Underline the sentence that **relates the writer's experience** to Bud.
2. Check three important **details** that describe the experience.
3. Number these details in the **time order** they happened.
4. Circle the **linking words** that connect the details.
5. Put a star before the sentences that **sum up** the writer's ideas and feelings.

Brainstorm

▶ Read the writing prompt in the middle of the idea web. Then use the boxes to help you brainstorm your ideas.

When have your friends helped you?

When have your family members helped you?

Writing Prompt:
Bud's pretend family helped him. Tell about a time when someone helped you. Describe what happened and tell how you felt.

When have people at school helped you?

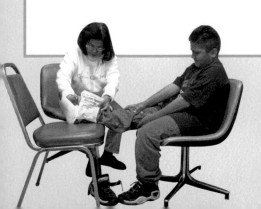

When have other people helped you?

Plan Your Paragraph

Writing Prompt: Bud's pretend family helped him. Tell about a time when someone helped you. Describe what happened and tell how you felt.

► Use this chart to plan and organize your paragraph.

Word Choices

_____

_____

_____

_____

_____

Introduce the Topic

- *Like Bud, I . . .*
- *A time when . . .*
- *There was a time when . . .*

Detail 1

- *It all started when . . .*
- *First, . . .*
- *First of all, . . .*

Detail 2

- *After that, . . .*
- *Then, . . .*
- *Next, . . .*

Detail 3

- *Finally, . . .*
- *In the end, . . .*
- *It got better after . . .*

Conclusion

- *I felt like . . .*
- *That's why . . .*
- *Overall, I felt . . .*

Write Your Paragraph

▶ Use this writing frame to write a first draft of your paragraph.

_____
(title)

Like Bud, I _____

_____

_____

It all started when _____

_____

_____

After that, _____

_____

_____

_____

Finally, _____

_____

_____

_____

I felt like _____

_____

_____

Revise

▶ Rate your paragraph. Then have a writing partner rate it.

Scoring Guide			
weak	okay	good	strong
1	2	3	4

1. Does the beginning **relate the writer's experience** to Bud?

Self	1	2	3	4
Partner	1	2	3	4

2. Are there **details** that describe the experience?

Self	1	2	3	4
Partner	1	2	3	4

3. Are details arranged in the **time order** they happened?

Self	1	2	3	4
Partner	1	2	3	4

4. Do **linking words** connect the details?

Self	1	2	3	4
Partner	1	2	3	4

5. Does the ending **sum up** the writer's ideas and feelings?

Self	1	2	3	4
Partner	1	2	3	4

▶ Now revise your paragraph to make it stronger.

Literature Response | Edit

Grammar CORRECTING RUN-ON SENTENCES

A **run-on sentence** is made up of two complete thoughts that are incorrectly joined together.

- To fix a run-on sentence, separate the ideas into two **complete sentences**.
- Or, insert a comma and a connecting word between the thoughts.

Example

Run-on sentence:	Bud woke up late he ran to get in line.
Complete sentences:	Bud woke up late. He ran to get in line.
Complete sentence:	Bud woke up late, so he ran to get in line.

▶ **Put an R next to each run-on sentence. Put a C next to each complete sentence.**

1. Bud walked along the line it went around two corners. _____R_____

2. Bud was hungry he decided to tell a lie. _____

3. The man pulled out a strap, and Bud was scared. _____

4. A tall man grabbed Bud he shook him. _____

5. A woman pointed to her feet two kids stood by her. _____

6. Bud was grateful, but he didn't like being slapped. _____

▶ **Rewrite the run-on sentences below as complete sentences.**

7. A lady was serving oatmeal she put some into Bud's bowl.

   _____

   _____

8. They ate oatmeal the kids got brown sugar, too.

   _____

9. The man laughed he thought Bud was funny.

   _____

10. The boy stuck out his tongue Bud did not mind.

   _____

 Take a close look at each of the sentences in your draft on page 77. Are any of them run-on sentences? If so, fix them.

Usage USING CORRECT WORD ORDER

The **order of words** in a sentence must make sense.

- An adjective comes before the noun it describes.
- A helping verb comes just before the main verb in a statement.

Example

Correct	Incorrect
Bud was a funny kid.	Bud was a kid funny.
Bud liked what he was eating.	Bud liked what was he eating.

▶ **Find and correct five errors in this paragraph.**

Student Model

A time when someone helped me was when was I learning to read. First, my sister older would read to me at night. Then, she taught me the sounds the letters make. Finally, when I had trouble with my homework, she gave me hints. I needed the extra help to imprve. Overall, my sister was like the family that helped Bud she made me really greatful.

Check and Correct

- ❑ Circle two spelling errors and correct them.
- ❑ Underline two word order errors and correct them.
- ❑ Correct one run-on sentence.

Edit *Look at the sentences in your draft on page 77. Do they all use correct word order? If not, fix them.*

Final Draft/Present

▶ **Write a final draft of your paragraph on paper or the computer. Check it again and correct any errors before you present it.**

Christopher Paul Curtis

Christopher Paul Curtis was raised in Flint, Michigan. After high school, he went to work in a car factory. He hung doors on new cars all day long. But during that time, he also started writing a book.

His wife thought he should try writing full time. So Curtis took a year off from his job. He finished his first book, *The Watsons Go To Birmingham—1963*. It won many awards, and readers loved it. The book changed Curtis's life. He quit his car factory job for good. *Bud, Not Buddy* is his second novel. It has also won many awards.

Curtis is known for his great sense of humor. His books are about funny characters. But they are also about important, and sometimes sad, events in America's history.

BOOKS:
- The Watsons Go to Birmingham—1963
- Bud, Not Buddy

"**Writers have to have really good ears and really good eyes. Ideas come from everywhere —sometimes from everyday conversations. They start really small and they grow, like planting a seed.**"

Ask Yourself

1. **Underline** ▶ Where did Curtis grow up?

2. **Circle** ▶ What was Curtis's job before becoming a writer?

3. Reread Curtis's quote. What does he mean by "really good ears and really good eyes"?

_____

_____

Evaluating a Book Review

How can you tell if you'll like a book? You can read a review of it. A book review gives a summary of the book. It also gives the reviewer's opinion. Read this review of *The Watsons Go To Birmingham—1963* by Christopher Paul Curtis.

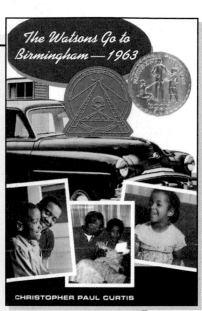

The Watsons Go To Birmingham—1963 is a great novel. It's about 10-year-old Kenny Watson and his wacky family. The book is funny, but it also deals with serious ideas.

Byron is Kenny's older brother. He's always getting into trouble. So Mr. and Mrs. Watson decide to drive the whole family from Michigan to Birmingham, Alabama. That way, Byron can spend time with his grandmother. She is strict and will keep him in line.

But in Birmingham, there's a tragedy. A church is bombed. This part of the book is based on a real church bombing that happened in 1963. Four young girls were killed in the bombing.

This is a terrific book. Anyone who reads it will really enjoy it. They will also learn about an important time in American history.

▶ **Fill in the circle next to each correct answer.**

1. What is the reviewer's opinion of the book?
Ⓐ She thinks it is too silly.
Ⓑ She thinks it is poorly written.
Ⓒ She thinks it is a wonderful book.
Ⓓ She doesn't like the strict grandmother.

2. What is the book about?
Ⓐ the Watson family
Ⓑ Birmingham, Alabama
Ⓒ car trips
Ⓓ grandmothers

3. Which of these is a sad event from the book?
Ⓐ a fight
Ⓑ a bombing
Ⓒ a car trip
Ⓓ a divorce

4. Does the reviewer think you will like this book?
Ⓐ yes
Ⓑ no
Ⓒ She's not sure.
Ⓓ She doesn't care.

5. A main reason to read a book review is to find out:
Ⓐ how the story ends.
Ⓑ the price of the book.
Ⓒ if it's at the library.
Ⓓ if others liked the book.

Comprehension

▶ **Fill in the circle next to the correct answer.**

1. In the story, what is Bud's main problem?

Ⓐ He is hurt.

Ⓑ He is hungry.

Ⓒ He is lost.

Ⓓ He is mad.

For short-answer questions, restate the question in your answer. This helps focus your answer.

2. When does this story take place?

Ⓐ in the present day

Ⓑ in the future

Ⓒ in the 1930s during the Depression

Ⓓ in the time of the Civil War

3. Bud's pretend parents help him by _____ .

Ⓐ letting him get in line with them

Ⓑ becoming friends with the man at the mission

Ⓒ telling him he should have gotten there earlier

Ⓓ giving him their oatmeal

4. Which pair of words best describes Bud's pretend parents?

Ⓐ selfish but funny

Ⓑ mean but smart

Ⓒ unhappy but giving

Ⓓ tough but caring

5. What do you think will happen the next time Bud goes to the food line?

Ⓐ Bud will become friends with the man with the strap.

Ⓑ Bud's pretend family will ignore him.

Ⓒ Bud will try to get to the mission early.

Ⓓ Bud will find a new pretend family.

Vocabulary

▶ **Fill in the circle next to the correct definitions of the underlined words.**

1. Bud was very <u>grateful</u> for the hot meal.
- Ⓐ hungry
- Ⓒ ready
- Ⓑ thankful
- Ⓓ happy

2. Will Bud's situation <u>improve</u>?
- Ⓐ get better
- Ⓒ get bigger
- Ⓑ get worse
- Ⓓ get smaller

3. There wasn't much food <u>available</u>, so having brown sugar was a <u>privilege</u>.
- Ⓐ useless; refusal
- Ⓒ possible to get; special advantage
- Ⓑ edible; punishment
- Ⓓ able to be cooked; against the law

▶ **Choose the correct definition for the underlined homophone.**

4. I had to be <u>patient</u> until the school bell rang.
- Ⓐ able to wait calmly
- Ⓒ adult help
- Ⓑ new ideas
- Ⓓ a person treated by a doctor

▶ **Choose the correct word from the word family.**

5. The children _____ have brown sugar with their oatmeal.
- Ⓐ normal
- Ⓒ normalize
- Ⓑ abnormal
- Ⓓ normally

Short Answer

▶ **Use what you've read in this Workshop to answer the question below. Check your spelling and grammar.**

Do you think that Bud is a survivor? Explain why.

_____

_____

_____

_____

Workshop 4
Nonfiction

Comprehension Focus
Summarize

READINGS
1 Stop All Bullies! >> Letter
2 Girl Fight >> Magazine Article
3 Bullying: Get the Facts >> Life Skills Feature

BULLIES BEWARE

Hitting. Punching. Pushing. That's only some of what bullies do. They also tease, put down, and embarrass other kids.

Do *you* know how to handle a bully? In this Workshop, you'll learn how to spot a bully. You'll find out why bullies push others around. And you'll get tips on how you can fight back!

VOCABULARY BUILDER

◎ **Target Word** ▶ Read the Target Words. Rate each one using the scale below.*	**Meaning** ▶ Read the Target Word meanings. Write in the missing ones.	**Example** ▶ Finish the Target Word examples. Write in the missing ones.
convince con•vince *(verb)* ① ② ③		My friend **convinced** me to try in-line skating.
expert ex•pert *(noun)* ① ② ③	someone with special knowledge or skills	
pressure pres•sure *(noun)* ① ② ③		Sometimes, I feel pressure to . . .
struggle strug•gle *(noun)* ① ② ③	something that is hard to do	
unite u•nite *(verb)* ① ② ③		My friends and I are united in our belief that . . .

*Rating Scale
① = I don't know it at all.
② = I've seen it before.
③ = I know it and use it.

The Big Idea

Write▶ What is this letter mainly about?

_____

_____

_____

VOCABULARY BUILDER

Target Word

insist

in•sist (verb)

Rate it: ① ② ③

Meaning

_____

_____

Example

_____

_____

_____

React

Would you want to start an anti-bullying group in your school? Why or why not?

September 15, 2005

Dear Principal Martinez:

Bullying is a big problem at our school. Kids are scared and upset. We want to stop all bullies now.

Last week, there was a bad case of bullying in the cafeteria. A group of fifth graders bullied a third grader. They told him to eat mashed potatoes mixed with mustard. The third grader said no. However, the bullies **insisted**. Everybody else was too afraid to help.

In fact, most kids at our school are afraid of bullies. We talked to the kids in our class. Over half said they were scared of being bullied. They were also afraid to stand up to bullies.

Bullying is bad because it can affect a kid's whole life. The victims of bullies can't focus on their schoolwork. Sometimes they even stay home from school. Worst of all, some victims turn into bullies themselves.

For these reasons, we want to start an anti-bullying club. We are asking for your support. If we all unite against bullies, we can stop them for good.

Sincerely,

Melissa Wilson   *Derek Johnson*   José Diego

Words to Know! **affect** to influence or change

Comprehension Focus
Summarize

A **summary** is a short statement that tells the most important ideas in a reading. To summarize:

- Find the topic of the reading.
- Look for the most important details about the topic.
- Restate the topic and important details in a short summary. Use your own words.

▶ Fill in this chart with the topic and important details in "Stop All Bullies!"

Topic

_____

Details

1. A group of fifth graders forced a third grader to eat mashed potatoes mixed with mustard. _____

2. _____

_____

3. _____

_____

Summarize

▶ Now, summarize the article. Check that you:
  ☐ state the topic
  ☐ give important details
  ☐ use your own words

💡 The Big Idea

Write ▶ What is this article mainly about?

_____

_____

_____

◎ Target Word

physical

phys•i•cal (adjective)

Rate it: ①   ②   ③

Meaning

_____

_____

Example

_____

_____

_____

❗ React

You read about three girls who were bullied. Which one do you think was hurt most? Why?

GIRL FIGHT

HOW DO GIRLS FIGHT? MEET THREE GIRLS WHO WERE BULLIED—BY OTHER GIRLS.

Just like boys, girls can be mean, tough bullies. But often, they don't get caught. That's because most girl bullies don't bully in obvious ways. Instead of throwing punches, girls may use words that hurt worse than any scratch or bruise.

WORDS HURT

Girl bullies often tease their victims about how they look. Bullies teased Keesha Washington because she wore glasses. Girls in Keesha's class called her names like four-eyes. For Keesha, just getting through class was a struggle.

Other girls make fun of their victims' families. Karen Williams had been a foster kid. Finally, she was adopted by a family. When Karen started sixth grade at her school, a popular girl bullied her. The

Do mean words hurt as much as punches?

bully laughed about Karen's home life. "She made fun of me because I was adopted," Karen says. "She was really mean. She picked on me because my mom and dad aren't my birth parents."

ALL ALONE

Girls who are bullied feel all alone. Often, no one talks to them or helps them out. All through middle school, kids called Kelsey Dodge names. They tried to make her cry. "If kids stuck up for me, they'd get bullied, too," she says.

Like Kelsey, most victims of teasing and name-calling have a tough time finding help. **Physical** bullying leaves marks you can see, like bruises. But no one can see the pain left by a bully's mean words. That's why girl bullies are hard to stop. ➡

Words to Know!	**obvious** clear, easy to see

 Summarize

1. **Write** What is the topic of the section "Words Hurt"?

_____

_____

_____

2. **Underline** Find two details in "Words Hurt" that relate to the topic.

3. Summarize the section "Words Hurt" in your own words. Tell your summary to a partner.

4. **Write** What is the topic of the section "All Alone"?

_____

_____

_____

_____

5. **Underline** Find two details in "All Alone" that relate to the topic.

6. Summarize the section "All Alone" in your own words. Tell your summary to a partner.

Active Reading

 Star ▶ Who says that she'll fight against bullying all her life?

VOCABULARY BUILDER

 Target Word

nervous

ner•vous *(adjective)*

Rate it: ①   ②   ③

Meaning

_____

_____

Example

_____

_____

_____

_____

React

Write ▶ Where would you go for help if you were bullied?

_____

_____

_____

_____

BULLIES ON THE RUN

How can you stop girls who bully? It's not easy. Keesha told her mom and her teachers about her bullies. Nothing happened at first. Then, the bullies got physical. They threw food at Keesha in the lunchroom. Finally, they were suspended.

Girl bullies can also get physical.

Karen, the former foster child, also complained. She told her family and teachers about her bully. She convinced them to help her. In eighth grade, Karen and the bully were put in different classes.

Kelsey never found help with her bullies. She had only one choice: waiting them out. Finally, in high school, the bullying stopped.

BAD MEMORIES

Keesha, Karen, and Kelsey have different stories. However, their bad memories are the same. They remember being bullied as the worst time of their lives. Experts say that many bullied kids feel this way.

Keesha still feels sad when she thinks about her bullies. Karen is always **nervous** at school. And Kelsey says that she'll fight against bullying all her life. "I know how it feels to get picked on," she says. "I'm never going to sit back and let someone else be treated the way they treated me." ⟨END⟩

Words to Know!   **suspended**   forced to leave school

Comprehension Focus
Summarize

▶ Fill in this chart with the topic and important details in the article "Girl Fight."

Topic

_____

Details

1. _____

_____

2. _____

_____

3. _____

_____

Summarize

▶ Now, tell your summary to a partner. Check that you:

☐ state the topic

☐ give important details

☐ use your own words

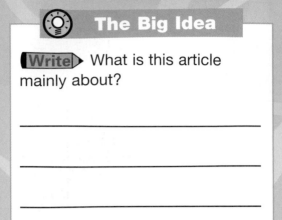

The Big Idea

Write What is this article mainly about?

_____

_____

_____

VOCABULARY BUILDER

Target Word

injure

in•jure (verb)

Rate it: ① ② ③

Meaning

_____

_____

Example

_____

_____

_____

React

Which is worse: hitting someone or gossiping about a friend?

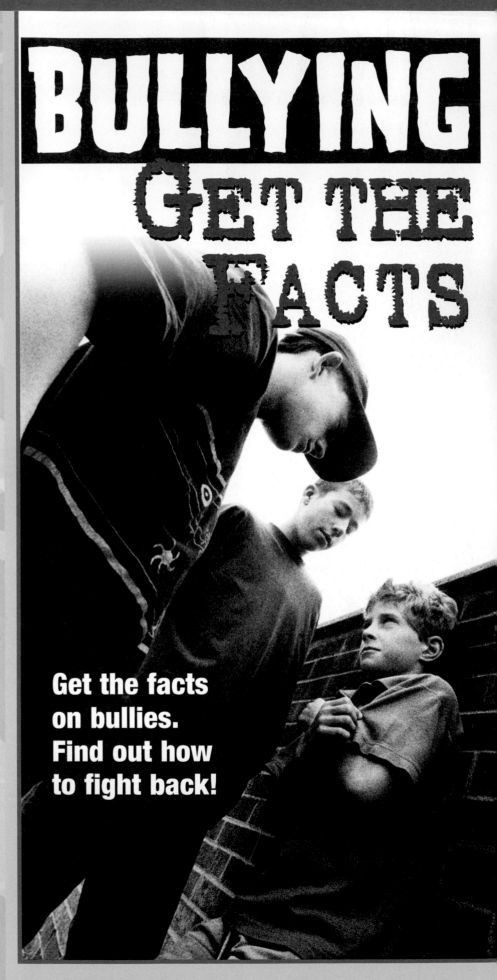

BULLYING GET THE FACTS

Get the facts on bullies. Find out how to fight back!

How They Attack

There are three different kinds of bullying. But they all have one thing in common. They make kids feel sad, hurt, and alone.

Most bullies hit, push, or trip their victims. This is called physical bullying—and it really hurts! However, bullies don't always **injure** kids physically.

There's another way to bully. It's called verbal bullying. That means hurting others with words. It includes name-calling and teasing.

There's a third kind of bullying. It's called relationship bullying. It starts when friends bully a kid in their group. They spread gossip, leave the kid out, or put on the pressure to do something wrong.

Who Is a Bully?

Why do some kids become bullies? It may seem like they were just born mean. But kids become bullies for a lot of different reasons.

Some kids are picked on at home. At first, their older brothers and sisters pick on them. Sometimes their parents do, too. Later, at school, these kids become bullies themselves. They want to make others feel as bad as they do.

Other kids want attention. They aren't happy unless all eyes are on them. They are convinced that they won't get enough attention by being good. So, they get it by being bad.

Finally, some kids are just spoiled! If your parents never teach you how to treat people, you might not know that bullying is wrong. Some parents think that their child is always right. Even when their child is a bully, the parents don't see it. ➡

Words to Know! **attention** paying special care to something

Summarize

1. **Write** What is the topic of "How They Attack"?

_____

_____

_____

2. **Underline** Find three details that relate to the topic.

3. Summarize the section in your own words. Tell your summary to a partner.

4. **Write** What is the topic of "Who Is a Bully?"

_____

_____

_____

5. **Underline** Find three important details in the section.

6. Summarize the section in your own words. Tell your summary to a partner.

Review: Sequence of Events

Circle Find the sequence words in "Who is a Bully?"

Active Reading

Star What percent of kids ages 12–15 feel pressure from bullies?

VOCABULARY BUILDER

◎ **Target Word**

incident
in•ci•dent (noun)

Rate it: ① ② ③

Meaning

_____

_____

Example

_____

_____

_____

_____

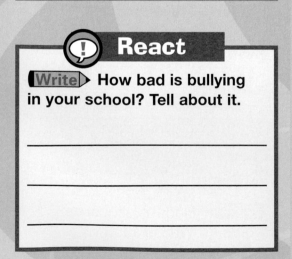

! **React**

Write How bad is bullying in your school? Tell about it.

_____

_____

_____

The Bully's Victim

Who do bullies like to pick on? Most bullies look for easy targets. They want to feel powerful. They get a kick out of making kids cry. So they target kids who get upset and cry easily.

Bullies also pick on kids who don't look like everyone else. Their victims might be smaller or bigger than other kids. They might be kids who wear glasses or braces. Sometimes, bullies choose victims who belong to a different race or religion.

However, bullying can be a problem for all kids. Experts say that more than half of all kids ages 8–11 are worried about bullies. For older kids, the problem is even worse. Sixty-eight percent of kids ages 12–15 feel pressure from bullies. So, being a bully's victim is more common than you think.

Fighting Back

What can you do to deal with a bully? There are many ways to fight back without fists. Check out these tips:

• **Control your emotions.** Bullies want to see you get upset. So, try not to let them see you cry. Walk away. Or, tell them to stop in a calm voice.

• **Help the victims.** If you see someone bullying someone else, try to stop it. Let victims know that they don't deserve the abuse. Kids with friends are less likely to get bullied.

• **Tell an adult.** Don't be afraid to tell an adult if you see a bullying **incident**. Your parents and teachers want you to be safe at school. Many schools have guidelines that protect victims. Know the rules—and be ready to fight back. **END**

Words to Know!   **abuse** harmful treatment of someone

TEXT FEATURE Reading a Bar Graph

What Worries Kids

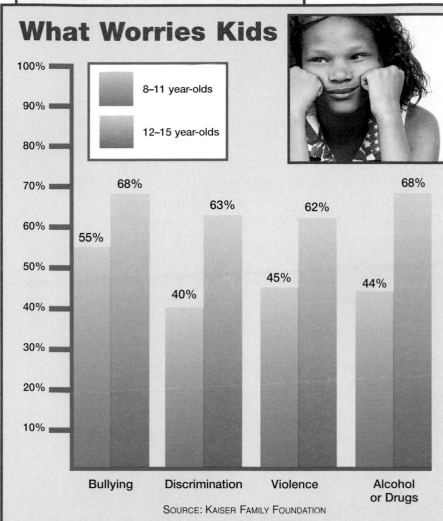

Legend:
- 8–11 year-olds
- 12–15 year-olds

Bars:
- Bullying: 55%, 68%
- Discrimination: 40%, 63%
- Violence: 45%, 62%
- Alcohol or Drugs: 44%, 68%

SOURCE: KAISER FAMILY FOUNDATION

A bar graph shows how information can be compared.

1. What information does this double bar graph show?

  Ⓐ the kinds of young people who fear bullies
  Ⓑ the problems two groups of kids worry about
  Ⓒ where bullied students live
  Ⓓ the percentage of 8–11 year-olds
     and 12–15 year-olds who bully

2. What color bar represents the 8–11 year-olds?

  Ⓐ green   Ⓑ blue
  Ⓒ yellow   Ⓓ orange

3. What percentage of 8–11 year-olds say that
   bullies are a big problem?

_____

 Summarize

1. **Write** What is the topic of the section "The Bully's Victim"?

_____

_____

_____

2. **Underline** Find two details in the section "The Bully's Victim" that relate to the topic.

3. Summarize the section in your own words. Tell your summary to a partner.

 Skills Check

1. **Write** What is the topic of the section "Fighting Back"?

_____

_____

_____

2. **Underline** Find three important details in "Fighting Back" that relate to the topic.

3. Turn to a partner. Summarize the section to a partner in your own words.

Take the WORD CHALLENGE

START

1 **Check two.** Which two activities would be the biggest struggle for you?

☐ making a three-point shot in basketball

☐ writing a scary story

☐ spelling a big word

☐ cooking a family dinner

✳ ✳ ✳ ✳ ✳

2 **Fill in.** Complete the following sentences using injured, incident, and insisted.

A few days ago, there was a

scary _____ on

the soccer field. My best friend

_____ his leg

pretty badly. We _____

that he go to a doctor.

3 **Context Clues**
Sometimes, you'll see a word you don't know in a sentence. One way to figure out what it means is to look at the words around it. The words around it are the "context" for the word. They can give you "context clues."

> I won a gold medal for my **extraordinary** physical talent.

What does *extraordinary* mean? Study the context and make a guess.

☐ common, boring   ☐ special, unusual

☐ ugly, weird   ☐ funny

4 **Choose two.** You're a major movie star, and you're away from home making a movie. Which two services would you insist on having?

☐ your own limo and driver

☐ your favorite video games in your hotel room

☐ your favorite snacks on the movie set

☐ a personal trainer to work out with you

✳ ✳ ✳ ✳ ✳ ✳ ✳

5 **Evaluate.** What is your favorite physical activity?

_____

What is your least favorite physical activity?

_____

What new physical activity would you like to try?

_____

6

Think about it. How do the people in your life put pressure on you? Write about it below.

My family pressures me to

_____

My friends pressure me to

_____

My teachers pressure me to

_____

I pressure myself to

_____

7

Check them. Read the problems below. Which ones would you need an expert's help with?

☐ your bike gets a flat tire

☐ your dog gets a bad cut on its paw

☐ you have to pick out a gift for your mom

☐ your email is not working

9

Rank them. Which situation would make you the most nervous? Put them in order.
1 = least
4 = most

____ taking a big math test

____ shooting a free throw in a championship basketball game.

____ jumping off the high diving board

____ baby-sit a younger sibling

❊ ❊ ❊ ❊ ❊

8

Compound Words

A **compound word** is made up of two smaller words. For example: Home + work = *homework.*

Match a word from the first column with a word from the second column to make a compound word.

Word 1 + Word 2 = Compound Word

foot	star	1._____
touch	ball	2._____
super	down	3._____

Now use the compound words to complete the sentence.

During the _____

game, I made a _____

and became a _____ .

base+ball = baseball

10

Fill in. Complete the following sentences using the words united, insists, and convince.

My best friend and I are

_____ in our view that

baseball is the best sport. But

I can't _____

her that hockey is a cool sport,

too. She _____

that hockey is boring.

FINISH

Writing Focus
Expository Summary

A summary gives the most important ideas and details from a reading.

▶ **Check out Diego's summary of the section "How They Attack" on page 93.**

Student Model

Summary of "How They Attack"

by Diego Francis

The section "How They Attack" describes the different ways that people bully. First, it tells about physical bullying, such as hitting and punching. Next, it describes verbal bullying, which includes teasing and name-calling. Then, the section describes relationship bullying. That's the kind of bullying where a kid is pressured or picked on by his or her own friends. Finally, the section says that all these kinds of bullying really hurt kids.

Parts of an Expository Summary

▶ **Find these parts of Diego's expository summary.**

1. Underline the sentence that states the **topic of the reading**.
2. Check three **important details**.
3. Circle the **linking words** that connect the details.
4. Reread to see that the summary is in the **writer's own words**.
5. Decide if the summary is **brief, but complete**.

Brainstorm

▶ Read the writing prompt in the middle of the idea web. Then, use the boxes to help you organize your ideas.

Topic

Important Detail

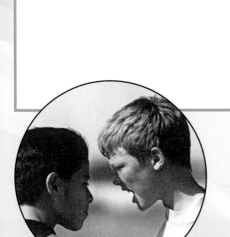

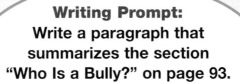

Writing Prompt:
Write a paragraph that summarizes the section "Who Is a Bully?" on page 93.

Important Detail

Important Detail

Plan Your Paragraph

Writing Prompt: Write a paragraph that summarizes the section "Who Is a Bully?"

▶ **Use this chart to plan and organize your paragraph.**

Word Choices

_____

_____

_____

_____

_____

Topic

- *The section "Who Is a Bully?" explains . . .*

- *There are different reasons why . . .*

- *The topic of the section "Who Is a Bully?" is . . .*

First Important Detail

- *First, it explains . . .*

- *One reason kids become bullies is . . .*

- *First of all, . . .*

Second Important Detail

- *Also, . . .*

- *A second reason is that . . .*

- *In addition, . . .*

Third Important Detail

- *In addition, . . .*

- *Another cause of bullying is . . .*

- *A third point is that . . .*

Last Important Detail

- *Finally, . . .*

- *Lastly, . . .*

- *A last point is . . .*

Write Your Paragraph

▶ Use this writing frame to write a first draft of your paragraph.

The section "Who Is a Bully?" describes _____
_____
_____

First, it explains _____
_____
_____

Also, _____
_____
_____

In addition, _____
_____
_____

Finally, _____
_____
_____

Revise

▶ Rate your paragraph. Then have a writing partner rate it.

Scoring Guide			
weak	okay	good	strong
1	2	3	4

1. Does the first sentence state the **topic of the reading**?

Self	1	2	3	4
Partner	1	2	3	4

2. Does the summary contain only **important details**?

Self	1	2	3	4
Partner	1	2	3	4

3. Do **linking words** connect the details?

Self	1	2	3	4
Partner	1	2	3	4

4. Is the summary written in the **writer's own words**?

Self	1	2	3	4
Partner	1	2	3	4

5. Is the summary **brief, yet complete**?

Self	1	2	3	4
Partner	1	2	3	4

▶ Now revise your paragraph to make it stronger.

Grammar USING CORRECT VERB TENSE

The **tense** of a verb shows when the action happens.

- A **present-tense verb** shows action that is happening now.
- A **past-tense verb** shows action that took place in the past. Most past-tense verbs end in *-ed*.

Example

Present-Tense Verb	Past-Tense Verb
Bullies pick on some kids.	Bullies picked on my brother.
A bully teases my friend.	The bully teased her all last year.

▶ **Identify the tense of the verb in each sentence below by writing present or past on the line to the right.**

1. Girls in Keesha's class called her names. _____*past*_____

2. Some girls tease younger students. _____

3. A popular girl at school bullied Karen. _____

4. Karen complained to her family and teachers. _____

5. The principal helps protect students. _____

6. Karen and Keesha feel nervous at school. _____

▶ **Rewrite the sentences below using the past tense of the verb.**

7. Some kids at school want attention.

_____

8. Karen and Kelsey talk about the bullies.

_____

9. The teachers punish the bullies at my school.

_____

10. Those mean girls pick on the new student.

_____

 Take a close look at each of the sentences in your draft on page 101. Do they all use the correct verb tense? Fix the ones that don't.

Mechanics USING COMMAS IN A SERIES

Items in a series are separated by **commas**.

- A series is a list of the same kinds of words.
- Commas follow every item in the series except the last one.

Example

Correct	Incorrect
Kids, parents, and teachers all want bullying to end.	Kids parents and teachers all want bullying to end.

▶ **Find and correct five errors in this paragraph.**

Student Model

Summary of "How They Attack"

    The section "How They Attack" is about how kids bully. First, it says that fisical bullying includes hitting punching and pushing. Also, it says that verbal bullying is teasing and name-calling. In addition, it describes relationship bullying. That's when a student is presured by friends. Finally, the section says that bullying was always hurtful.

Check and Correct

- ❑ Circle two spelling errors and correct them.
- ❑ Underline two comma errors and correct them.
- ❑ Correct one verb tense error.

Edit   *Look at the sentences in your draft on page 101. Do they all use commas in a series correctly? Fix the ones that don't.*

Final Draft/Present

▶ **Write a final draft of your paragraph on paper or the computer. Check it again and correct any errors before you present it.**

Police Officer

Officer Nestor Figueroa works in the police department of Jacksonville, Florida. Like most police officers, he patrols the streets and answers emergency calls. But he also works with kids in schools, teaching them to avoid violence. "I feel like I'm making a difference," Figueroa says.

Name: Officer Nestor Figueroa

Hometown: Jacksonville, Florida

Job: Police Officer

Duties:
• protects the people of Jacksonville
• helps visitors find their way around
• stops crime
• teaches kids to avoid violence

Skills:
• ability to communicate clearly
• problem-solving skills

Similar Jobs:
• security guard
• military service personnel

Pay: $33,000 per year

Education: High school diploma and police officer school

Ask Yourself

1. **Underline** ▶ Mark the education needed for this job.

2. What question would you like to ask Officer Figueroa?

_____

_____

3. Would you want this job?

☐ Yes   ☐ Maybe   ☐ No

Using a Street Map

A police officer like Nestor Figueroa uses a street map to answer emergency calls or to help visitors find their way around. This is a map of Officer Figueroa's hometown of Jacksonville, Florida.

Look carefully at the street map below. Then answer the questions about it.

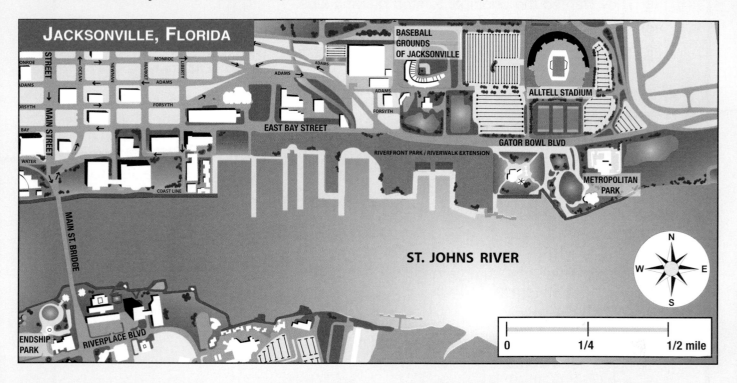

▶ **Fill in the circle next to each correct answer.**

1. Which street is Alltell Stadium on?

Ⓐ Riverplace Blvd.

Ⓑ Gator Bowl Blvd.

Ⓒ East Bay Street

Ⓓ Main Street

2. Which river does the Main Street Bridge cross?

Ⓐ Alltell River

Ⓑ Main River

Ⓒ St. Johns River

Ⓓ Main Street River

3. Which park is nearest to Alltell Stadium?

Ⓐ Metropolitan Park

Ⓑ Friendship Park

Ⓒ St. John's Park

Ⓓ Gator Bowl Park

4. Approximately how long is Main Street Bridge?

Ⓐ 1/4 mile

Ⓑ 2 miles

Ⓒ 4 miles

Ⓓ 5 miles

5. Which direction would you go to get from the Main Street Bridge to Metropolitan Park?

Ⓐ north

Ⓑ east

Ⓒ south

Ⓓ west

Comprehension

▶ **Fill in the circle next to the correct answer.**

1. What purpose did the authors of the "Stop All Bullies!" letter have?

    Ⓐ They wanted to get a bully kicked out of school.

    Ⓑ They wanted the principal to stop bullying kids.

    Ⓒ They wanted to start an anti-bullying group at school.

    Ⓓ They wanted all fifth-grade bullies to be punished.

2. If you are the victim of a girl bully, why might it be hard to get help?

    Ⓐ 911 does not respond to calls for help.

    Ⓑ Many girl bullies tease, which is not as obvious as physical fighting.

    Ⓒ People don't believe that girls can bully.

    Ⓓ The fights are loud.

> **Here's a Tip!**
> Always fill in bubbles completely when you are taking multiple-choice tests. If you don't, the computer might not be able to read your answer.

3. Which sentence best summarizes the article "Girl Fight"?

    Ⓐ Girls never fight.

    Ⓑ Girls don't usually throw punches so their fights don't matter.

    Ⓒ Girls usually fight verbally, but it's just as serious as fighting physically.

    Ⓓ Girls are very good at dealing with the problem of bullying.

4. Bullies usually pick on kids who seem _____.

    Ⓐ hard to upset   Ⓒ hard to talk to

    Ⓑ easy to upset   Ⓓ popular

5. Approximately how many kids ages 8–11 are worried about bullies?

    Ⓐ over half of all kids

    Ⓑ almost all kids

    Ⓒ only a few kids

    Ⓓ none of them

Vocabulary

▶ **Fill in the circle next to the correct definitions of the underlined words.**

1. Winning the championship game would be a <u>struggle</u> unless we were <u>united</u>.
   - Ⓐ a shock; sad
   - Ⓒ a really fun experience; injured
   - Ⓑ a test; beaten
   - Ⓓ something that is hard to do; came together

2. <u>Experts</u> agree that dealing with school bullies can be difficult.
   - Ⓐ kids
   - Ⓒ a bully's victims
   - Ⓑ teachers
   - Ⓓ people with special knowledge or skills

3. Dina <u>convinced</u> the principal that kids were under <u>pressure</u> from bullies.
   - Ⓐ told; friendship
   - Ⓒ apologized to; a bully's victim
   - Ⓑ ignored; cheating
   - Ⓓ made someone believe; strong influence

▶ **Pick the definition of the underlined word by using context clues.**

4. My cousin is so <u>obstinate</u>, you can't convince her to do anything!
   - Ⓐ easy to please
   - Ⓒ stubborn
   - Ⓑ funny-looking
   - Ⓓ happy

▶ **Which word in this sentence is a compound word?**

5. The principal explained the school guidelines to the new students.
   - Ⓐ principal
   - Ⓒ students
   - Ⓑ school
   - Ⓓ guidelines

Short Answer

▶ **Use what you've read in this Workshop to answer the question below. Check your spelling and grammar.**

What is one thing you could do to stop bullying in your school? Explain how you would do it.

_____

_____

_____

Workshop 5

Nonfiction

SECRETS OF THE MUMMY'S TOMB

Thousands of years ago, kings called pharaohs ruled Egypt. When a pharaoh died, his body was made into a mummy. Then the mummy was placed in a large pyramid filled with gold, jewels, and even pets!

For years, the mummies kept their secrets. Then explorers and scientists opened the tombs. Inside, they found amazing treasures.

Turn the page to discover the secrets of the mummy's tomb.

VOCABULARY BUILDER

◎ Target Word ▶ Read the Target Words. Rate each one using the scale below.*	Meaning ▶ Read the Target Word meanings. Write in the missing ones.	Example ▶ Finish the Target Word examples below. Write in the missing ones.
construct con•struct (verb) ① ② ③		Egyptians **constructed** pyramids thousands of years ago.
examine ex•am•ine (verb) ① ② ③	to investigate or look into something	
material ma•te•ri•al (noun) ① ② ③		Materials used to build a house include . . .
preserve pre•serve (verb) ① ② ③	to keep something from being destroyed	
symbol sym•bol (noun) ① ② ③		Some symbols of America are . . .

*Rating Scale
① = I don't know it at all.
② = I've seen it before.
③ = I know it and use it.

The Big Idea

Write What is this article mainly about?

_____

_____

VOCABULARY BUILDER

  Target Word

investigate

in•ves•ti•gate (verb)

Rate it: ① ② ③

Meaning

_____

_____

Example

_____

_____

_____

 **React**

Do you think it would be fun to search for mummies? Or would it be boring and hard?

KING TUT'S TOMB

The mummy case of King Tut.

King Tut ruled Egypt for only a few years. But his tomb was one of the greatest discoveries of all time.

A scientist and explorer named Howard Carter found the tomb. He began searching for it in 1914. He looked in a part of Egypt called the Valley of the Kings. By 1922, Carter had a big problem. He was out of money. His team wanted to give up the search.

But Carter wasn't ready to quit. He was convinced that he should **investigate** a little longer. Later that year, Carter found an old stairway. It was buried under a pile of stones. When the stones were cleared away, he saw something exciting. The stairway led to a door. It was the door to King Tut's tomb!

Carter's long years of searching were worth it. Many ancient tombs had been robbed of their treasures. But Tut's tomb was barely touched. Its many rooms were packed with gold and jewels!

Only one problem remained. Where was Tut's mummy? Carter examined every room. Finally, he located it deep inside the tomb. Today Tut is the most famous mummy in the world! **END**

Words to Know!	**tomb** a burial chamber

Problem and Solution

A **problem** is a situation or event that causes trouble. A **solution** is what fixes the problem. To find a problem and its solution:

- Look for the problem.
- Find the solution to the problem.

▶ **Fill in this chart with two problems and solutions from "King Tut's Tomb."**

Problem
_____
_____
_____
_____
_____

Solution
_____
_____
_____
_____
_____

Problem
_____
_____
_____
_____

Solution
_____
_____
_____
_____

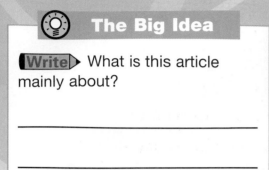

The Big Idea

Write ▶ What is this article mainly about?

_____

_____

VOCABULARY BUILDER

Target Word

task

task (noun)

Rate it: ① ② ③

Meaning

_____

_____

Example

_____

_____

_____

React

Would you touch a mummy if you could? Why or why not?

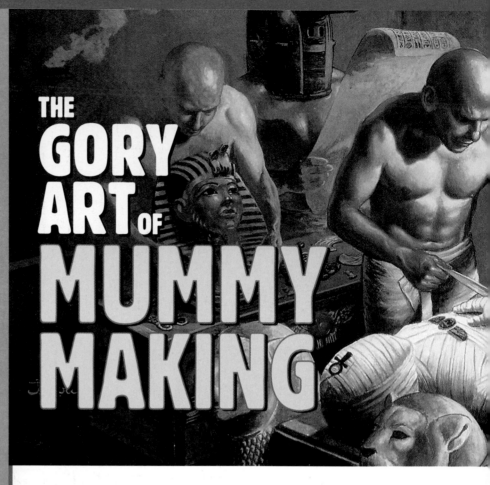

THE GORY ART OF MUMMY MAKING

How to preserve a dead body before it rots!

Death was a whole new life for the ancient Egyptians. They believed that the dead went to live in another world. But there was one big problem. The dead needed their bodies to live in that world. And dead bodies rot fast. So the Egyptians found a way to solve the problem. They preserved dead bodies by making them into mummies.

Taking the Insides Out

When a body dies, its organs rot first. The organs are parts like the brain, eyes, liver, and lungs. The mummy makers' first **task** was to take out those parts. They used a special hook to remove the brain. The hook went up the body's nose. With each pull, a piece of brain popped out!

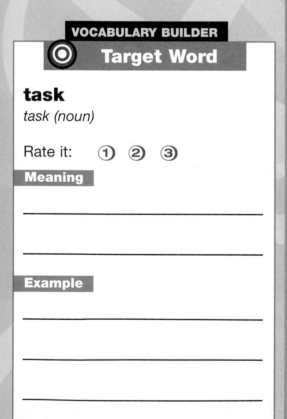

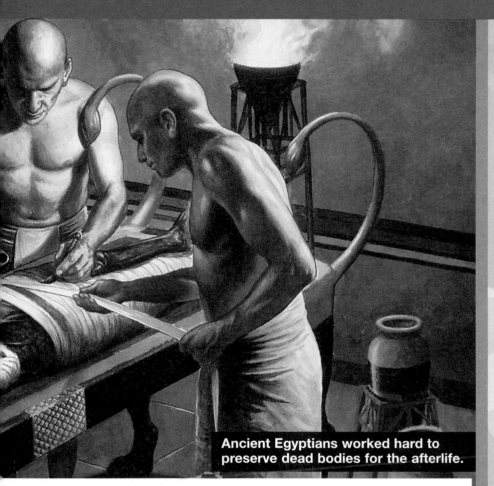

Ancient Egyptians worked hard to preserve dead bodies for the afterlife.

Dry as Bone

Next, the Egyptians dealt with another problem. Dead bodies are full of water. Water makes things rot. So, the mummy makers covered each body with salt. The salt absorbed water like a sponge. After 40 days, the body was dry as bone.

Next, it was time to make the body look nice. First, the Egyptians coated it with tree sap. The sap dried and became a hard shell. Then the mummy makers stuffed the body with rags. The rags helped it keep its shape. They even put false eyes into the face. Finally, the mummy was ready for wrapping. ➡

Words to Know!	**absorb** to soak up liquid

Problem and Solution

1. **Write** ▷ What problem did the mummy makers face?

_____

_____

_____

_____

_____

_____

_____

_____

2. **Underline** ▷ Find two ways that the mummy makers tried to solve this problem.

Active Reading

Star What might be included with a mummy in its case?

VOCABULARY BUILDER
Target Word

system

sys•tem *(noun)*

Rate it: ① ② ③

Meaning

_____

_____

Example

_____

_____

_____

_____

React

Write Would you want to see someone make a mummy in real life? Would that be cool—or gross?

_____

_____

_____

This cat was an Egyptian's pet. Now its mummy is on display at a museum.

All Wrapped Up

Once a body was dry, the Egyptians had one more problem. They needed to protect the body. So they wrapped the body in layers of cloth. First, they cut the cloth into long strips. Then they wound the strips around the head and body. Between the layers, they put jewels and good luck charms. Finally, they put a mask on the mummy. The mask looked like the dead person's real face.

Next, mummy makers constructed a special box. The box was called a mummy case. The dead person's favorite things were packed in the case. Symbols of their wealth were also put inside. Even dead pets were put in the mummy case! The pets were mummies, too, of course.

The Test of Time

How did the Egyptians' **system** work out? Some mummies are now over 2,000 years old! And they still look great. Examine them yourself. You can find them in museums around the world.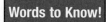

Words to Know!	**layer** something that is placed on or between other things

Problem and Solution

▶ Fill in this chart with problems and solutions from "The Gory Art of Mummy Making."

Problem

_____

_____

_____

_____

_____

Solution

_____

_____

_____

_____

Problem

_____

_____

_____

_____

Solution

_____

_____

_____

_____

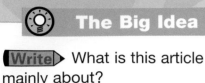
The Big Idea

Write What is this article mainly about?

_____

_____

VOCABULARY BUILDER

Target Word

transport

trans•port (verb)

Rate it: ① ② ③

Meaning

_____

_____

Example

_____

_____

_____

React

How would workers build a pyramid today? What tools might they use?

Ancient
Unlocking the Past

In Egypt, pyramids were the tombs of kings. Find out how pyramids were built!

Great Kings, Great Pyramids

The pyramids of Egypt are over 4,000 years old. They were built for the pharaohs, who were kings of Egypt. When a pharaoh died, his body was made into a mummy. Then the mummy was buried inside a pyramid.

Building a pyramid was a huge project. The average pyramid took twenty years to build! It also took lots of planning and supplies. To solve that problem, a pharaoh started planning his burial pyramid as soon as he came to power.

Getting Ready to Build

Preparing the pyramid site was hard work. The pyramid base had to be flat. Otherwise, the pyramid would be lopsided! So builders came up with a method for making the base flat. First, they dug trenches in the ground. Then they flooded the trenches. Bumps of sand appeared above the water. The sand was leveled off and made flat.

Builders also had to deal with another problem.

Egypt

Workers moved enormous blocks to build a pyramid.

The sides of the pyramid had to be exactly the same distance apart. If not, they wouldn't meet at the top! So, four priests marked where each side should go. First, they stood at the center of the site. Then, one priest walked north. Another walked east. The third went south. The fourth went west. They all walked the exact same distance from the center.

Getting materials to the site was a problem, too. Pyramids are made of huge, heavy stone blocks that are very hard to **transport**. So, workers carved the blocks out of cliffs next to the Nile River. In the summer, the river flooded. The water rose high. Then, workers could float the blocks across the river to the pyramid site.

➡

Words to Know!	**trenches** long, narrow ditches

📖 Problem and Solution

1. `Underline` ▶ Find the sentences that tell how the problem of making a flat base was solved.

2. `Write` ▶ What problem would there be if the sides weren't exactly the same distance apart?

_____

_____

_____

_____

3. `Circle` ▶ How did workers get the heavy blocks to the site of the pyramid?

📖 Review: Summarize

What is the topic of "Getting Ready to Build"? What are two important details? Summarize the section to a partner.

Active Reading

Star What was placed at the top of a pyramid?

VOCABULARY BUILDER

Target Word

value
val•ue (noun)

Rate it: ① ② ③

Meaning

_____

_____

Example

_____

_____

_____

_____

React

Write Would you be afraid to go into a pyramid? Why or why not?

_____

_____

_____

_____

Pushing Half-Ton Blocks

Once on land, the heavy blocks were hauled to the pyramid site. But this presented another problem. Moving heavy blocks was much harder on land than on water.

Workers found solutions. When the ground was smooth, they put wooden rollers under the blocks. Then they rolled the blocks to the site. But when the ground was rough, workers had to pull the blocks with ropes. One man shouted directions. The others yelled together. As they yelled, they pulled. That way, they were sure to pull at the same time.

Finally, the blocks were put in place, layer by layer. Each layer became a platform. The next layer was built on top. Workers constructed ramps made of mud to pull up each layer of blocks. At the very top, workers placed a miniature pyramid.

TEXT FEATURE Reading A Diagram

LAYOUT OF KING TUT'S TOMB

BURIAL CHAMBER

TREASURY

North

ANTECHAMBER

CORRIDOR

STAIRS

ANNEX

KEY
- Plaster Wall
- Room

Keeping Out Robbers

Before the pyramid was finished, a tomb was built deep inside it. The pharaoh's mummy was placed inside the tomb. The mummy was buried with many things of **value**, like money, jewels, and furniture. There was even a jar with the pharaoh's liver in it!

From the tomb, a passage led outside. It was the only way out. It was also a way in for tomb robbers. The pyramid builders tried to solve this problem. They made the door to the passage look like solid stone. They also built traps! In the dark, a robber might step on a fake stone. Then he'd fall into a deep hole. Sadly, these solutions didn't always work. Many tombs were robbed.

However, the great pyramids have lasted for many centuries. They are a symbol of ancient Egyptian culture. If you ever go to Egypt, you can still see them rising up from the sand. ⟨END⟩

Words to Know!	**centuries** periods of one hundred years

A diagram provides information with drawings and labels.

1. How many rooms are in King Tut's tomb?

   (A) five   (C) two
   (B) three   (D) six

2. What do the dark blue sections represent?

   (A) plaster walls   (C) guards
   (B) treasures   (D) traps for robbers

3. Why do you think there are so many walls between the stairs to the tomb and the burial chamber itself?

   _____

   _____

   _____

Problem and Solution

1. **Write** ▷ How did workers push the heavy blocks across land? Find two solutions.

   • _____

   _____

   • _____

   _____

2. **Underline** ▷ How did workers move the blocks up the pyramid?

Skills Check

1. **Write** ▷ What problem did the builders face after they put the pharaoh and his belongings in the pyramid?

   _____

   _____

   _____

   _____

2. **Underline** ▷ Find two ways they tried to solve this problem.

Take the WORD CHALLENGE

START

1 Estimate. How long would it take you to construct each of the following?

	Minutes
a snow fort	_____
a sandcastle on an ocean beach	_____
a sock puppet	_____

• • • • • •

2 Pick two. Which of the following are tasks?

Doing dishes	_____
Watching TV	_____
Talking to your friends	_____
Cleaning your room	_____

3 Homophones

I'm **rapping** a song.

I'm **wrapping** a present.

Homophones are words that sound alike but have different spellings and meanings. Examples are *piece* and *peace* and *wrap* and *rap*.

Match each word to its homophone below.

two	hear	week

	Homophone
here	_____
too	_____
weak	_____

Fill in each sentence with a homophone.

It's been a _____ since I saw my friend Ricky!

Please turn up the music, so I can _____ it better.

You're going swimming? I want to go _____!

4 Analyze. How much value do the items below have for you? Rank them from 1 to 4.

1 = least value   4 = most value

___ a bag of money

___ a book of family pictures

___ a special gift from your best friend

___ a shopping spree at the mall

• • • • • • • • •

5 Check it. Your pet snake is sick. What's the *least* dangerous way to transport it to the vet?

☐ around your neck   ☐ inside your backpack

☐ in a plastic bag   ☐ in a box with tiny breathing holes in it

6 **Think about it.** Examine the picture above. What kind of food do you think it is?

_____

_____

Would you eat it? Explain why or why not.

_____

_____

◆ ◆ ◆ ◆ ◆ ◆

7 **Rate it.** What's the best way to plan a birthday party?
1 = first choice   3 = last choice

_____ First, investigate your options by talking to your family and friends. Then, pass out invitations and celebrate!

_____ First, study the history of birthday parties. Next, create a system for organizing your party. Then, make a list of food, decorations, and people to invite.

_____ First, make a list of materials you'll need to make decorations. Then, tell your friends to make your decorations. Then, tell _them_ to throw _you_ a party.

8 **Idioms**
An idiom is a phrase that means something different from the separate meanings of the words in the phrase. Something interesting can be called "food for thought." Something easy to do is "a piece of cake."

I grew this plant on my own. I've got a real **green thumb**.

Match these idioms to their meanings:

"You're in hot water!"   You've got a big problem.

"I'm sick as a dog!"   You are very sick.

Now, finish these sentences:

I was in hot water after I _____.

I was sick as a dog when _____.

9 **Rate it.** How can you preserve a left-over sandwich? Rate these methods from 1 to 4.
1=best 4= worst

_____ wrap it in plastic   _____ put it in your pocket

_____ stuff it in your desk   _____ put it in the fridge

◆ ◆ ◆ ◆ ◆ ◆ ◆ ◆ ◆

10 **Think about it.** Write the word that each of these symbols stands for:

 _____  _____ _____

Now draw your own symbol and tell what it stands for:

_____

FINISH

Writing Focus
Persuasive Paragraph

A persuasive paragraph tries to convince the reader to share the writer's opinions.

▶ **Check out Hyeran's persuasive paragraph about why her class should take a trip to a museum.**

> **Student Model**
>
> **Why Our Class Should Go to the Museum**
>
> **by Hyeran Kim**
>
> I strongly believe that our class should take a trip to the museum. One reason is that the museum has a display that shows what life was like in ancient Egypt. A second reason is that museums give tours to teach large groups of kids. Most importantly, the museum has real mummies that we could examine. This would help us better understand what we've read. In conclusion, a class trip to a museum is a great idea.

Parts of a Persuasive Paragraph

▶ **Find these parts of Hyeran's persuasive paragraph.**

1. Underline the sentence that states the writer's **opinion**.
2. Check three **reasons** that support the opinion.
3. Put a box around the reason you think is **strongest**.
4. Circle the **linking words** that connect the ideas.
5. Put a star beside the sentence that **restates** the writer's opinion.

Brainstorm

▶ Read the writing prompt in the middle of the idea web. Then use the boxes to help you brainstorm your ideas.

Cool Things to See in Egypt

Things to Learn About in Egypt

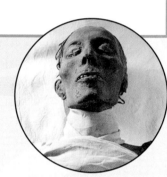

Writing Prompt:
Persuade your principal that your class should take a field trip to Egypt to see the mummies.

People You Could Meet in Egypt

Other Fun Things About the Trip

Plan Your Paragraph

Writing Prompt: Persuade your principal that your class should take a field trip to Egypt to see the mummies.

▶ Use this chart to plan and organize your ideas.

Word Choices

_____

_____

_____

_____

_____

Your Opinion

• *I strongly believe that . . .*

• *I am writing to recommend that . . .*

• *Please approve our class trip to . . .*

Reason 1

• *One reason is that . . .*

• *First of all, . . .*

• *We would all benefit because . . .*

Reason 2

• *A second reason is that . . .*

• *In addition, . . .*

• *Another important point . . .*

Reason 3

• *Most importantly, . . .*

• *The most important point . . .*

• *Finally, . . .*

Conclusion/Recommendation

• *In conclusion, . . .*

• *Overall . . .*

• *It's important that we . . .*

Write Your Paragraph

▶ Use this writing frame to write a first draft of your paragraph.

_____

(title)

I strongly believe that _____

_____

_____

One reason is that _____

_____

_____

A second reason is that _____

_____

_____

_____

Most importantly, _____

_____

_____

_____

In conclusion, _____

_____

_____

_____

Revise

▶ Rate your paragraph. Then have a writing partner rate it.

Scoring Guide			
weak	okay	good	strong
1	2	3	4

1. Does the first sentence clearly state the writer's **opinion**?

Self	1	2	3	4
Partner	1	2	3	4

2. Is the opinion supported by several **reasons**?

Self	1	2	3	4
Partner	1	2	3	4

3. Are the reasons given **strong and convincing**?

Self	1	2	3	4
Partner	1	2	3	4

4. Do **linking words** connect the ideas?

Self	1	2	3	4
Partner	1	2	3	4

5. Does the concluding statement **restate** the writer's opinion?

Self	1	2	3	4
Partner	1	2	3	4

▶ Now revise your paragraph to make it stronger.

Grammar USING IRREGULAR VERBS

Most past-tense verbs end in *-ed*. **Irregular verbs** do not.

- You must remember the different spellings of irregular past-tense verbs.
- The verb *to be* is a common irregular verb. Its **present-tense** forms are am, is, are. Its **past-tense** forms are was, was, were.

Example

Present-Tense Verb	Past-Tense Verb
Egyptians make the mummies.	Egyptians made the mummies.
The kings build pyramids.	The kings built pyramids.
The pyramids are made of stone.	The pyramids were made of stone.

▶ **Circle the correct past-tense verb in each sentence below.**

1. The search for King Tut [leaded (led)] Carter to Egypt.

2. Robbers [stealed stole] treasures from the tombs of many mummies.

3. The robbers never [found finded] the mummy of King Tut.

4. Carter [taked took] King Tut's treasures out of the tomb.

5. Workers [made maked] King Tut's tomb with many secret passages.

6. Carter was glad that he [goed went] to explore in Egypt.

▶ **Rewrite the sentences below using the past-tense form of the verb.**

7. The Egyptians **have** many rules for making mummies.

_____

8. Carter **sees** the mummy in a hidden back room.

_____

9. Many robbers **break** into the tombs.

_____

10. Some of them **fall** into traps in the floor.

_____

Edit ▶ *Look at each of the sentences in your draft on page 125. Do they all use the correct form of irregular verbs? Fix the ones that don't.*

Mechanics USING COMMAS WITH INTRODUCTORY WORDS

A **comma** follows an opening word or phrase at the beginning of a sentence.

- *Yes, First, Next*, and *Later* are opening words.
- *In addition* and *After a while* are opening phrases.

Example

Correct	Incorrect
Yes, King Tut was a pharaoh.	Yes King Tut was a pharaoh.
After a while, they found the tomb.	After a while they found the tomb.

▶ **Find and correct five errors in this paragraph.**

Student Model

> I think that our class should go to Egypt. First we could exemine the amazing pyramids that were builded years ago. In addition, we could talk to museum workers there about perserving mummies. Another reason is that it would be cool to take a trip on the Nile. In conclusion I think a trip to Egypt would be fun for the whole class.

Check and Correct
- ❑ Circle two spelling errors and correct them.
- ❑ Underline one verb tense error and correct it.
- ❑ Correct two comma errors.

 Edit *Look at the sentences in your draft on page 125. Are all opening words and phrases followed by a comma? Fix the ones that aren't.*

Final Draft/Present

▶ **Write a final draft of your paragraph on paper or the computer. Check it again and correct any errors before you present it.**

Careers

Construction Worker

Meet Kyosuke Otsuka. He has never built a pyramid, but he has built houses, buildings, and skyscrapers. His job as a construction worker requires teamwork, intelligence, and physical strength. "You must be willing to work hard," he says. "More importantly, you should get satisfaction from creating something with your hands."

Name: Kyosuke Otsuka

Hometown: New York City

Job: Construction Worker

Duties:
- construct frames for buildings
- build forms for concrete
- build walls, floors, and ceilings

Skills:
- good with your hands
- able to follow floor plans and directions
- basic math skills

Similar Jobs:
- Carpenter
- Bricklayer

Pay: $35,000 to $90,000 per year

Education: High school diploma

Construction workers build everything from houses, to skyscrapers, to bridges and tunnels.

Ask Yourself

1. **Underline** ▶ Mark the level of education needed for this job.

2. Would you rather work inside or outside? Explain.

_____

_____

3. Would you want this job?

☐ Yes ☐ Maybe ☐ No

Interpreting a Floor Plan

When he builds houses and skyscrapers, Kyosuke uses a floor plan. It gives a basic outline of the building and the rooms in it. Look at this apartment floor plan. Then, answer the questions that follow.

Floor Plan for an Apartment

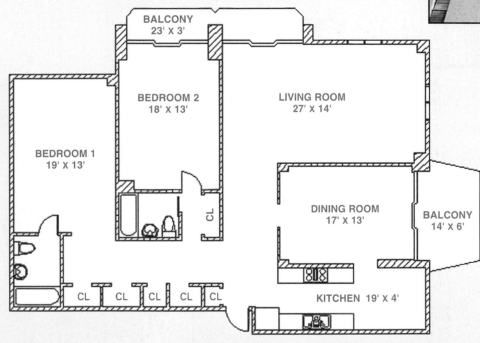

BALCONY
23' X 3'

BEDROOM 2
18' X 13'

LIVING ROOM
27' X 14'

BEDROOM 1
19' X 13'

CL

DINING ROOM
17' X 13'

BALCONY
14' X 6'

CL   CL   CL   CL   CL

KITCHEN 19' X 4'

▶ **Fill in the circle next to the correct answer.**

1. Without doing any math, which room seems to be the biggest?

- Ⓐ the kitchen
- Ⓑ the living room
- Ⓒ the dining room
- Ⓓ the bedroom

2. What is the length of the living room?

- Ⓐ 17'
- Ⓑ 14'
- Ⓒ 27'
- Ⓓ 18'

3. Which rooms are connected to the dining room?

- Ⓐ the kitchen and bedroom
- Ⓑ the living room and kitchen
- Ⓒ both bedrooms
- Ⓓ bedroom and bathroom

4. How many closets are in this apartment?

- Ⓐ three
- Ⓑ four
- Ⓒ five
- Ⓓ six

5. How many bathrooms are there in the apartment?

- Ⓐ two
- Ⓑ none
- Ⓒ three
- Ⓓ one

Comprehension

▶ **Fill in the circle next to the correct answer.**

Here's a tip!
Some questions ask for your opinion. Be sure to back up your thoughts with text evidence.

1. Why is King Tut famous?

Ⓐ He is the current pharaoh of Egypt.

Ⓑ His tomb was one of the most famous finds in Egypt.

Ⓒ He had the largest pyramid in Egypt.

Ⓓ Many robbers died trying to open his tomb.

2. What problem was solved by wrapping the mummies in layers of cloth?

Ⓐ The cloth kept mummies warm.

Ⓑ The cloth helped mummies recover from broken bones.

Ⓒ The cloth fooled robbers.

Ⓓ The cloth protected the mummies after they were dried out.

3. How did mummy makers get the brain out of a dead body?

Ⓐ They cut open the skull and removed it.

Ⓑ They pulled the brain out through the nose.

Ⓒ They melted the brain and poured it out the ears.

Ⓓ They waited for the brain to rot away.

4. How did pyramid builders use the Nile River?

Ⓐ They used mud from the river for bricks.

Ⓑ They floated stone blocks across the river.

Ⓒ They coated the pyramids with river mud.

Ⓓ They used water from the river for a pond.

5. What is one way robbers were kept out of the pyramids?

Ⓐ Wild dogs were locked in the pyramids.

Ⓑ Trap doors with deep pits were built in the pyramids.

Ⓒ Ghosts haunted the pyramids.

Ⓓ Poison clouds were released when the pyramids were opened.

Vocabulary

▶ **Fill in the circle next to the correct definitions of the underlined words.**

1. Scientists <u>examine</u> mummies to discover how they were made.
   - Ⓐ to find
   - Ⓒ to look into or to investigate
   - Ⓑ to make
   - Ⓓ to preserve

2. The pyramids were <u>constructed</u> out of <u>materials</u> from nearby cliffs.
   - Ⓐ ugly; waste
   - Ⓒ built; things used to make other things
   - Ⓑ held up; glue
   - Ⓓ moved; neighborhoods

3. The pyramids are <u>preserved</u> because they are a <u>symbol</u> of Egypt's history.
   - Ⓐ repaired; stone
   - Ⓒ forgotten; a big lie told to escape something
   - Ⓑ destroyed; piece
   - Ⓓ kept from being destroyed; a sign

▶ **Mark the idiom that fits best in this sentence.**

4. When I caught the flu, I was _____ for two weeks.
   - Ⓐ happy as a clam
   - Ⓒ sick as a dog
   - Ⓑ mad as a hatter
   - Ⓓ sad as a tear

▶ **Mark the word that fits best in this sentence.**

5. To keep it fresh, I will _____ my sandwich in plastic.
   - Ⓐ wrap
   - Ⓒ rep
   - Ⓑ rap
   - Ⓓ rip

Short Answer

▶ **Use what you've read in this Workshop to answer the question below. Check your spelling and grammar.**

Why do you think people are still interested in the ancient Egyptians?

_____

_____

_____

_____

Comprehension Focus
Story Elements

READINGS
1 The Marble Champ >> Short Story
2 S-T-R-E-T-C-H >> Poetry

GOOD SPORTS

Have you ever wanted to be a champ? Would you work hard enough to make it happen?

Author Gary Soto worked hard to become a famous writer. Lupe Medrano works hard, too. She's the main character in Soto's story, "The Marble Champ."

Lupe wants to be the best marbles player on the playground. What will it take for her to succeed?

VOCABULARY BUILDER

◎ Target Word ▶ Read the Target Words. Rate each one using the scale below.*	Meaning ▶ Read the Target Word meanings. Write in the missing ones.	Example ▶ Finish the Target Word examples below. Write in the missing ones.
accurate ac•cu•rate (adjective) ① ② ③		It is important to be accurate when . . .
encourage en•cour•age (verb) ① ② ③	to praise or offer support	
energy en•er•gy (noun) ① ② ③		This meal will give me lots of **energy**.
opponent op•po•nent (noun) ① ② ③	someone who is against you in a game	
strengthen strength•en (verb) ① ② ③		I can strengthen my muscles by . . .

*Rating Scale
① = I don't know it at all.
② = I've seen it before.
③ = I know it and use it.

Comprehension Focus

Story Elements

A **short story** like "The Marble Champ" is a brief work of fiction. It focuses on one or two main characters and on a single problem or conflict. To understand a short story, look for four elements:

1. **Setting** is where and when a story takes place.
   This story takes place in present-day Fresno, California.

2. **Characters** are the people in the story. The main character is the most important character. These are the characters in this story:

Lupe Medrano,
a twelve-year-old girl

Lupe's parents

Lupe's brother

3. **Plot** is the sequence of events in a story. The plot contains a problem that the main character needs to solve. In "The Marble Champ," Lupe is good at a lot of things. The problem is, she's no good at sports. Can she ever become a marble champ?

4. **Theme** is the big message of the story. It's what the author wants us to think about or remember.

▶ **Turn the page to begin reading Lupe's story.**

THE MARBLE CHAMP

▶ **Fill in this chart as you reread the story.**

	Part 1 (pp. 136–139)	**Part 2** (pp. 140–145)	**Part 3** (pp. 146–149)
Setting	Time: One afternoon Place: Lupe's house in Fresno, California	Time: Place:	Time: Place:
Character	Who is the main character? Describe him/her:	How does the character change?	What is the character like now?
Plot Events	What happens at the beginning of the story?	What happens in the middle of the story?	How does the story end?
Theme	Author's message:		

Active Reading

Write What kind of runner is Lupe?

_____

_____

React

Write What is something you're good at?

_____

_____

_____

_____

THE MARBLE CHAMP

by GARY SOTO

Lupe Medrano, a shy girl who spoke in whispers, was the school's spelling bee champion. She was also the winner of the reading contest at the public library three summers in a row, the blue ribbon awardee in the science fair, and the top student at her piano recital. Lupe was even the playground grand champion in chess. She was a straight-A student and—not counting kindergarten, when she had been stung by a wasp—never missed one day of elementary school. She had received a small trophy for this honor and had been congratulated by the mayor.

Lupe had a razor-sharp mind. But she could not make her body, no matter how much she tried, run as fast as the other girls. She begged her body to move faster, but could never beat anyone in the fifty-yard dash.

The truth was that Lupe was no good in sports.

➡

Setting

1. **Write** Look at the picture. Where do you think Lupe might be?

_____

_____

_____

_____

Character

2. **Underline** Find three things that Lupe is good at.

Plot

3. **Write** What problem does Lupe have?

_____

_____

_____

_____

_____

_____

☀ Active Reading

> **Star** ▶ What sport does Lupe decide to play?

VOCABULARY BUILDER

◎ Target Word

previous

pre•vi•ous (adjective)

Rate it: ① ② ③

Meaning

_____

_____

Example

_____

_____

_____

_____

❗ React

What do you think Lupe should do to improve her marbles game?

She could not catch a pop-up or figure out in which direction to kick the soccer ball. One time she kicked the ball at her own goal and scored a point for the other team. She was no good at baseball or basketball either. She even had a hard time making a hula hoop stay on her hips.

It wasn't until last year, when she was eleven years old, that she learned how to ride a bike. And even then she had to use training wheels. She could walk in the swimming pool but couldn't swim. And she chanced roller skating only when her father held her hand.

"I'll never be good at sports," she fumed one rainy day. She was laying on her bed gazing at the shelf her father had made to hold her awards. "I wish I could win something, anything, even marbles."

At the word "marbles," she sat up. "That's it. Maybe I could be good at playing marbles." She hopped out of bed and rummaged through the closet. Finally, she found a can full of her brother's marbles. She poured the rich glass treasure on her bed and picked five of the most beautiful marbles.

Words to Know!   **gazing** looking at something for a long time

"I wish I could win something, anything, even marbles."

She smoothed her bedspread. Then she practiced shooting, softly at first so that her aim would be accurate. The marble rolled from her thumb and clicked against the targeted marble. But the target wouldn't budge. She tried again and again. Her aim became accurate. But the power from her thumb made the marble move only an inch or two. Then she realized that the bedspread was slowing the marbles. She also had to admit that her thumb was weaker than the neck of a newborn chick.

She looked out the window. The rain was letting up, but the ground was too muddy to play. She sat cross-legged on the bed, rolling her five marbles between her palms. Yes, she thought, I could play marbles. And marbles is a sport. At that moment she realized that she had only two weeks to practice. The playground championship, the same one her brother had entered the **previous** year, was coming up. She had a lot to do. ➡

Story Elements

Setting
1. **Circle** ▸ Lupe practices marbles in her bedroom. Find a detail that lets you know this.

Character
2. **Write** ▸ What word would you use to describe Lupe's feelings about playing marbles?

_____

_____

Plot
3. **Write** ▸ How does Lupe start to solve her problem?

_____

_____

_____

_____

_____

_____

Now go to page 135. Add details to Part 1 of the chart.

Literature

Active Reading

Star What advice does Lupe's brother give her about playing marbles?

VOCABULARY BUILDER
Target Word

exhaustion

ex•haus•tion (noun)

Rate it: ① ② ③

Meaning

_____

_____

Example

_____

_____

_____

_____

React

Write Do you think Lupe has what it takes to be a marble champ? Why or why not?

_____

_____

_____

_____

She squeezed a rubber eraser one hundred times, hoping it would strengthen her thumb.

• • • • • • • • • • • • • • • • • •

To strengthen her wrists, she decided to do twenty push-ups on her fingertips, five at a time. "One, two, three . . ." she groaned. By the end of the first set she was breathing hard. Her muscles burned from **exhaustion**. She did one more set and decided that was enough push-ups for the first day.

She squeezed a rubber eraser one hundred times, hoping it would strengthen her thumb. This seemed to work because the next day her thumb was sore. She could hardly hold a marble in her hand, let alone send it flying with power. So Lupe rested that day and listened to her brother. He gave her tips on how to shoot: get low, aim with one eye, and place one knuckle on the ground.

"Think 'eye and thumb'—and let it rip!" he said.

After school the next day she left her homework in her backpack. She practiced three hours straight, taking time only to eat a candy bar for energy. With a popsicle stick, she drew an odd-shaped circle and tossed in four marbles. She used her shooter, a milky agate with hypnotic swirls, to blast them. Her thumb *had* become stronger.

After practice, she squeezed the eraser for an hour. Lupe ate dinner with her left hand to spare her shooting hand. She said nothing to her parents about her dreams of athletic glory. ➡

Setting

1. **Write** Where does the action in this part of the story take place?

_____

_____

Character

2. **Write** How has Lupe changed herself?

_____

_____

_____

_____

Plot

3. **Write** What is Lupe doing to become a better marbles player?

_____

_____

_____

_____

_____

Active Reading

Write Who does Lupe beat at marbles?

_____

_____

_____

React

Do you think Lupe is nervous about the championship? Why or why not?

Practice, practice, practice. Squeeze, squeeze, squeeze. Lupe got better and beat her brother. Then she beat Alfonso, a neighbor kid who was supposed to be a champ.

"Man, she's bad!" Alfonso said. "She can beat the other girls for sure. I think."

The weeks passed quickly. Lupe worked so hard that one day, while she was drying dishes, her mother asked why her thumb was swollen.

"It's muscle," Lupe explained. "I've been practicing for the marbles championship."

"You, honey?" Her mother knew Lupe was no good at sports.

"Yeah, I beat Alfonso. And he's pretty good."

That night, over dinner, Mrs. Medrano said, "Honey, you should see Lupe's thumb."

"Huh?" Mr. Medrano said, wiping his mouth and looking at his daughter.

"Show your father."

"Do I have to?" an embarrassed Lupe asked.

"Go on, show your father."

Reluctantly, Lupe raised her hand and flexed her thumb. You could see the muscle.

The father put down his fork. He asked, "What happened?"

"Dad, I've been working out. I've been squeezing an eraser."

"Why?"

"I'm going to enter the marbles championship."

Her father looked at her mother and then back at his daughter. "When is it, honey?"

"This Saturday. Can you come?"

Words to Know! **reluctantly** not wanting to do something

The father had been planning to play racquetball with a friend Saturday. But he said he would be there. He knew his daughter thought she was no good at sports. He wanted to encourage her. He even rigged some lights in the backyard so she could practice after dark. He squatted with one knee on the ground, entranced by the sight of his daughter easily beating her brother.

The day of the championship began with a cold blustery sky. The sun was a silvery light behind slate clouds.

"I hope it clears up," her father said. He rubbed his hands together as he returned from getting the newspaper. They ate breakfast and paced nervously around the house waiting for 10:00 to arrive. Then they walked the two blocks to the playground (though Mr. Medrano wanted to drive so Lupe wouldn't get tired). She signed up and was assigned her first match on baseball diamond number three. ➡

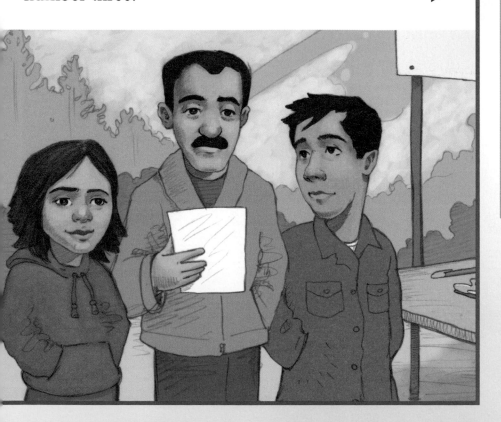

Setting
1. **Circle** What is the weather on the day of the championship?

Write Where does the championship take place?

_____

Character
2. **Underline** Lupe is becoming a better marbles player. Find an example that shows this.

Plot
3. **Write** What important things happen in this part of the story?

_____

_____

_____

_____

_____

_____

_____

Literature

 Active Reading

Star How does Lupe do in her first match?

VOCABULARY BUILDER

 Target Word

proceed
pro•ceed (verb)

Rate it: ① ② ③

Meaning

_____

_____

Example

_____

_____

_____

_____

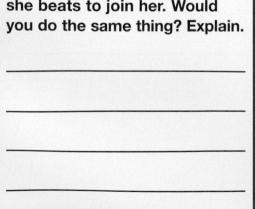 **React**

Write Lupe invites the girls she beats to join her. Would you do the same thing? Explain.

_____

_____

_____

_____

Lupe, walking between her brother and her father, shook from the cold, not nerves. She took off her mittens, and everyone stared at her thumb. Someone asked, "How can you play with a broken thumb?" Lupe smiled and said nothing.

> **"Just think of the marbles, not the girl. And let your thumb do the work."**

She beat her first opponent easily. She felt sorry for the girl because she didn't have anyone to cheer for her. Except for her sack of marbles, she was all alone. Lupe invited the girl, whose name was Rachel, to stay with them. She smiled and said, "OK." The four of them walked to a card table in the middle of the outfield, where Lupe was assigned another opponent.

She also beat this girl, a fifth-grader named Yolanda. Lupe asked her to join their group. They **proceeded** to more matches and more wins. Soon there was a crowd of people following Lupe to the finals to play a girl in a baseball cap. This girl seemed dead serious. She never even looked at Lupe.

"I don't know, Dad, she looks tough."

Rachel hugged Lupe and said, "Go get her."

"You can do it," her father encouraged. "Just think of the marbles, not the girl. And let your thumb do the work."

The other girl broke first and earned one marble. She missed her next shot. Lupe, one eye closed, her thumb quivering with energy, blasted two marbles out of the circle but missed her next shot. Her opponent earned two more before missing. She stamped her foot and said "Shoot!" The score was three to two in favor of Miss Baseball Cap.

The referee stopped the game. "Back up, please, give them room," he shouted. Onlookers had gathered too tightly around the players. ➡

Words to Know! | quivering shaking

Story Elements

Setting
1. **Circle** ▶ What effect does the cold weather have on Lupe?

Character
2. **Write** ▶ Lupe makes friends with the girls she beats. What does that say about her?

_____

_____

_____

_____

Plot
3. **Write** ▶ How is Lupe doing in the championship?

_____

_____

_____

_____

_____

_____

Now go to page 135. Add details to Part 2 of the chart.

Active Reading

Write Who wins the final match?

_____

_____

_____

VOCABULARY BUILDER

Target Word

rely

re•ly (verb)

Rate it: ① ② ③

Meaning

_____

_____

Example

_____

_____

_____

React

Have you ever been in a competition? How did you feel?

Lupe then earned three marbles. She was set to get her fourth when a gust of wind blew dust in her eyes. She missed badly. Her opponent quickly scored two marbles, tying the game, and moved ahead six to five on a lucky shot. Then she missed. Lupe, whose eyes felt scratchy when she blinked, **relied** on instinct and thumb muscle to score the tying point. It was now six to six, with only three

Words to Know! **instinct** a natural feeling

marbles left. Lupe blew her nose and studied the angles. She dropped to one knee, steadied her hand, and shot so hard she cracked two marbles from the circle. She was the winner!

"I did it!" Lupe said under her breath. She rose from her knees, which hurt from bending all day, and hugged her father. He hugged her back and smiled.

Everyone clapped, except Miss Baseball Cap. She made a face and stared at the ground. Lupe told her she was a great player, and they shook hands. A newspaper photographer took pictures of the two girls standing shoulder-to-shoulder, with Lupe holding the trophy.

➡️

Story Elements

Setting

1. **Circle** ▶ Find how the wind affects Lupe's game.

Character

2. **Check** ▶ Which word best describes how Lupe acts during the tournament?

Ⓐ nervous

Ⓑ confident

Ⓒ careless

Ⓓ mean

Plot

3. **Write** ▶ What important event happens in this part of the story?

_____

_____

_____

_____

_____

Literature

 Active Reading

 Star What does Lupe think at the end of the story?

VOCABULARY BUILDER

 Target Word

display
dis•play *(verb)*

Rate it: ① ② ③

Meaning

_____

_____

Example

_____

_____

_____

_____

 React

 Write Think of something that you would like to do well. What could you do to improve that skill?

_____

_____

_____

_____

"You did it, thumb. You made me champion."

Lupe then played the winner of the boys' division. After a poor start, she beat him eleven to four. She blasted the marbles, shattering one into sparkling slivers of glass. Her opponent looked on glumly as Lupe did what she did best—win!

The head referee and the President of the Fresno Marble Association stood with Lupe as she **displayed** her trophies for the newspaper photographer. Lupe shook hands with everyone, including a dog who had come over to see what the commotion was all about.

That night, the family went out for pizza. They set the two trophies on the table for everyone in the restaurant to see. People came up to congratulate Lupe. She felt a little embarrassed, but her father said the trophies belonged there.

Back home, in the privacy of her bedroom, she placed the trophies on her shelf and was happy. She had always earned honors because of her brains. But winning in sports was a new experience. She thanked her tired thumb. "You did it, thumb. You made me champion." As its reward, Lupe went to the bathroom and filled the bathroom sink with warm water. She let her thumb swim and splash as it pleased. Then she climbed into bed and drifted into a hard-won sleep. **END**

| Words to Know! | **commotion** noisy, excited activity |

Story Elements

Setting
1. **Circle** Where does Lupe's family go to celebrate?

Character
2. **Underline** How does Lupe feel about the attention she gets at the restaurant?

Theme
3. **Check** Which is a theme of this story?
(A) Parents should encourage their children.
(B) If you work hard, you can achieve a goal.
(C) Be kind to your opponent.
(D) More people should play marbles.

Now go to page 135. Complete Part 3 of the chart and the theme.

Skills Check

1. **Underline** Find a sentence that shows that Lupe is proud of herself.

2. **Write** How has Lupe solved her problem?

_____

_____

_____

_____

Active Reading

Write What is the "awful problem" that the poem's narrator has with basketball?

_____

_____

_____

S·T·R·E·T·C·H

by Gordon Korman & Bernice Korman

Basketball is everything!
It's always been my dream
To deke and sky and dunk and fly,
And play for my school team.

But there's an awful problem
No one can seem to fix:
The team height starts at six foot four,
And I am four foot six.

 React

Do you think this poem is humorous or serious? Why?

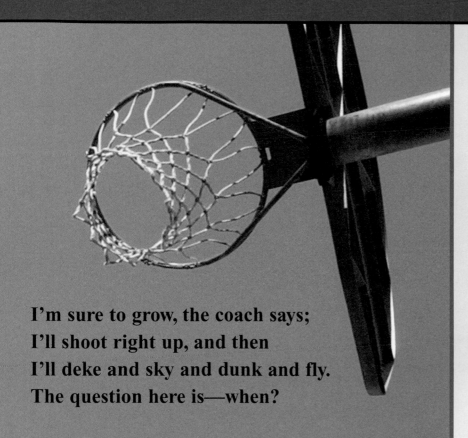

I'm sure to grow, the coach says;
I'll shoot right up, and then
I'll deke and sky and dunk and fly.
The question here is—when?

It might take till I'm thirty,
That's what I greatly fear,
For I'll no longer be in school—
(Miss Mott says I'll be here.)

I've got to do some growing
(Is there a stretching pill?),
I won't be here at thirty!
(Miss Mott says yes, I will.)

I shall not be discouraged,
I'll never shut the door.
Someday when I sit on the bench
My feet will reach the floor!

I'll make it to the court, then,
To play for my school team.
I'll deke and sky and dunk and fly—
It's always been my dream.

 **Literary Elements:
Rhyme**

Rhyme is two or more words that have ending syllables with the same sound.

Circle ▸ Find the words that rhyme in the poem.

 **Literary Elements:
First-Person Narrator**

A narrator is the person who tells a story. A **first-person narrator** tells a story using the word "I."

Underline ▸ Find two things that the narrator of this poem tells about himself.

TAKE THE WORD CHALLENGE

START

1 **Check them.** Which of these activities takes *a lot* of energy?

☐ sleeping

☐ running

☐ doing math

☐ swimming

2 **Decide.** Which of these would strengthen a friendship?

☐ helping your friend study for a test

☐ talking behind your friend's back

☐ giving your friend a present

☐ ignoring your friend

3 **Multiple-Meaning Words**
Multiple-meaning words are words that have more than one meaning. For example, the *goal* is where you must put the ball to score points in a game. But a *goal* is also something that you want to do or achieve.

Read each sentence. Then check the correct meaning of *energy* in that sentence.

I ate a snack. Now I have energy for practice.

☐ strength　　☐ time　　☐ electricity

Leaving the lights on is a waste of energy.

☐ strength　　☐ time　　☐ electricity

My **goal** is to put the ball in the **goal**.

4 **Tell about it.** Think about the people below. What do you rely on each of them for?

Your best friend: _____

Your parents: _____

The police in your town: _____

• • • • • • • • • • • • • • • • • • • •

5 **Fill in.** To get an **accurate** measurement of your weight, use a _____.

To get an **accurate** measurement of

the temperature, use a _____.

To get an **accurate** measurement

of height, use a _____.

6

Decide. Put a **Y** next to displays you would want to see. Put an **N** next to displays you wouldn't want to see.

_____ a stamp collection

_____ the latest sports cars

_____ movie star posters

_____ a shoe collection

_____ dinosaur bones

7

Circle one in each row. Would you feel exhaustion from . . .

walking **OR** running?

staying awake **OR** sleeping?

watching TV **OR** studying?

gym class **OR** music class?

8

Word Families

A **word family** is a group of words that share the same base word and have related meanings, such as _courage, encourage,_ and _discourage. Courage_ means "bravery" or "strength." _Encourage_ means "to give someone courage or help." _Discourage_ means "to lessen or take away someone's courage."

This took **courage.** I'm glad you **encouraged** me!

Complete the sentences. Use the correct form of _courage._

1. It takes a lot of _____ to stick up for what you believe in.

2. The coach gave us a pep talk to _____ us before the big game.

3. I want to try snowboarding, but my parents think it's too dangerous. They keep trying to _____ me.

9

Fill it in. Fill in the blanks with opponents and previous.

My soccer team is getting ready for the big game. Our

_____ won their _____ game.

But we're pretty sure we can beat them.

10

Think about it. Finish these sentences.

If there's a fire, **proceed** to the nearest _____.

If you hit a baseball, **proceed** to _____.

When you get to school, **proceed** to your _____.

FINISH

Writing Focus

Literature Review

A **literature review** presents the reviewer's opinion of a story.

▶ **Read Sanjay's literature review of "Bud's Breakfast," the story in Workshop 3.**

Student Model

A Literature Review of "Bud's Breakfast"
by Sanjay Patel

I thought "Bud's Breakfast" was an excellent story. First of all, Bud was a funny character. He always had humorous things to say, even when he was in trouble. Also, the setting of the story taught me about the Great Depression. I didn't know that people didn't have enough to eat then. Finally, I liked the story because the family was nice to him. Bud was able to rely on them for help. In conclusion, I really enjoyed this story and encourage everyone to read it.

Parts of a Literature Review

▶ **Find these parts of Sanjay's literature review.**

1. Underline the sentence that clearly states the **writer's opinion** of the story.
2. Check three specific **reasons** that support the opinion.
3. Put a box around the reason you think is **strongest**.
4. Circle the **linking words** that connect the ideas.
5. Put a star before the sentence that **sums up** the writer's opinion.

Brainstorm

▶ Read the writing prompt in the middle of the idea web. Then use the boxes to help you brainstorm your ideas.

Setting

Characters

Writing Prompt:
Explain your opinion of "The Marble Champ." Did you think it was an excellent, average, or weak story?

Plot

Theme

Plan Your Paragraph

Writing Prompt: Explain your opinion of "The Marble Champ." Did you think it was an excellent, average, or weak story?

▶ **Use this chart to plan and organize your paragraph.**

Word Choices

_____

_____

_____

_____

_____

Statement About the Story

- *I thought . . .*

- *The story . . .*

- *In my opinion, . . .*

Example or Reason 1

- *First of all, . . .*

- *The first reason . . .*

- *To start with, . . .*

Example or Reason 2

- *Also, . . .*

- *Another reason why . . .*

- *The second reason . . .*

Example or Reason 3

- *Finally, . . .*

- *The third reason . . .*

- *In addition, . . .*

Concluding Statement

- *In conclusion, . . .*

- *I recommend . . .*

- *I do not recommend . . .*

Write Your Paragraph

▶ Use this writing frame to write a first draft of your paragraph.

_____
(title)

I thought _____

_____

_____

First of all, _____

_____

_____

Also, _____

_____

_____

_____

Finally, _____

_____

_____

_____

In conclusion, _____

_____

_____

_____

_____

Revise

▶ Rate your paragraph. Then have a writing partner rate it.

Scoring Guide			
weak	okay	good	strong
1	2	3	4

1. Does the beginning clearly state the **writer's opinion** of the story?

Self   1   2   3   4

Partner   1   2   3   4

2. Are there specific **reasons** that support the opinion?

Self   1   2   3   4

Partner   1   2   3   4

3. Are the reasons given **strong and convincing**?

Self   1   2   3   4

Partner   1   2   3   4

4. Do **linking words** connect the ideas?

Self   1   2   3   4

Partner   1   2   3   4

5. Does the ending **sum up** the writer's opinion?

Self   1   2   3   4

Partner   1   2   3   4

▶ Now revise your paragraph to make it stronger.

Grammar SUBJECT-VERB AGREEMENT

The **subject and verb** in a sentence must agree in number.

- A verb that agrees with a **singular subject** tells what one person, place, or thing is doing. It usually ends in *-s* or *-es*.

- A verb that agrees with a **plural subject** tells what more than one person or thing is doing. It usually does not end in *-s* or *-es*.

Example

Singular Subject	Plural Subject
The marble rolls across the ground.	The marbles roll across the ground.
Lupe squeezes an eraser.	We squeeze erasers, too.

▶ **Put an X next to the sentence if it has subject-verb agreement errors. Put a check if the sentence is correct.**

1. Sometimes, Lupe kick the ball into her own goal. _____X_____

2. She rides a bike with training wheels. _____

3. Every day, Lupe practice shooting marbles on her bed. _____

4. Her muscles burns from exhaustion. _____

5. Her brother and father gives her some hints. _____

6. Lupe enters the marble championship. _____

▶ **Rewrite the following sentences with correct subject-verb agreement. (Be sure to keep all the sentences in present tense.)**

7. Several girls follows Lupe from game to game.

_____

8. Lupe's father cheer for her.

_____

9. Miss Baseball Cap stare at the ground.

_____

10. Lupe win the game against the boys' champ.

_____

 Take a close look at each of the sentences in your draft on page 157. Do the subjects and verbs all agree? If not, fix them.

Mechanics USING POSSESSIVES

A **possessive noun** shows ownership.

- Add an apostrophe (') and an -s to a singular noun.
- Add an apostrophe to a plural noun that ends in -s.

Example

Correct	Incorrect
Lupe's brother gave her advice.	Lupes brother gave her advice.
She looked at the marbles' colors.	She looked at the marbles colors.

▶ **Find and correct five errors in this paragraph.**

Student Model

I thought "Bud's Breakfast" was a weak story. To start with, I didn't like Bud. He shouldn't reliye on his charm to get in the breakfast line. Also, Bud was not grateful for the familys help. Finally, I thinks that the family should have proceded to let Bud live with them. Then Buds life would have been easier. I do not recommend this story.

Check and Correct

- ❏ Circle two spelling errors and correct them.
- ❏ Underline two errors with possessives and correct them.
- ❏ Correct one subject-verb agreement error.

Edit *Look at the sentences in your draft on page 157. Are all the possessive nouns formed correctly? If not, fix them.*

Final Draft/Present

▶ **Write a final draft of your paragraph on paper or the computer. Check it again and correct any errors before you present it.**

Good Sports **159**

Meet the Author

Gary Soto

BOOKS:
- *Baseball in April and Other Stories* (this book contains "The Marble Champ")
- *Petty Crimes*
- *Crazy Weekend*
- *Summer on Wheels*

POETRY:
- *Neighborhood Odes*
- *Fearless Fernie*

Like Lupe Medrano from "The Marble Champ," Gary Soto grew up in Fresno, California. He was born there in 1952. When he was growing up, Soto thought he would become a scientist. He wanted to study dinosaur bones. But when he was in college, Soto discovered a book of poetry. After that, he decided to become a writer.

Soto uses his childhood as a basis for many of his books, stories, and poems. Often they are set in Fresno's Mexican-American community.

Soto says he spent much of his childhood at Fresno's Romain playground. He calls the place "an education in itself." No wonder so many of his stories, like "The Marble Champ," have playgrounds in them!

"**I discovered that reading builds a life inside the mind.**"

Ask Yourself

1. **Underline** ▸ Where did Gary Soto grow up?

2. **Circle** ▸ Mark which of Gary Soto's books or poetry sounds the most interesting to you.

3. How much do you want to be a writer?

   ❑ I don't want it.
   ❑ I might want it.
   ❑ I really want it.

Reading an Author Home Page

Where can you learn more about Gary Soto? Authors often have Web sites. The home page of a Web site is its main page. The home page connects you to other pages. Check out the home page of Gary Soto's Web site below.

▶ **Fill in the circle next to each correct answer.**

1. What is this Web site about?

- Ⓐ Lupe Medrano
- Ⓑ baseball
- Ⓒ Fresno, California
- Ⓓ Gary Soto

2. What is the address of this Web site?

- Ⓐ www.garysoto.com
- Ⓑ www.welcome.com
- Ⓒ www.officialwebsite.com
- Ⓓ www.home.com

3. Which button would you click to find out what books you can order?

- Ⓐ FAQ (frequently asked questions)
- Ⓑ his photo
- Ⓒ Home
- Ⓓ Catalog

4. What are you most likely to see if you click "FAQ"?

- Ⓐ a book order form
- Ⓑ a biography of Gary Soto
- Ⓒ frequently asked questions that people ask Gary Soto
- Ⓓ pictures of Gary Soto's family

5. Who would be most likely to go to this Web site?

- Ⓐ someone who likes Fresno, California
- Ⓑ someone who likes Gary Soto's books
- Ⓒ someone who likes buying magazines
- Ⓓ someone who is learning how to use the Internet

Comprehension

▶ **Fill in the circle next to the correct answer.**

1. In the story, what is Lupe's main problem?

    Ⓐ She is a bad student.

    Ⓑ She has an important race coming up.

    Ⓒ She is bad at sports.

    Ⓓ She has a sore thumb.

2. Lupe decides to become good at marbles by _____.

    Ⓐ buying a lot of marbles

    Ⓑ practicing

    Ⓒ reading about marbles

    Ⓓ cheating

Here's a tip.

Some short-answer questions ask for your opinion. Be sure to back up your thoughts with text evidence.

3. Which pair of words best describes Lupe?

    Ⓐ sad and angry

    Ⓑ smart and determined

    Ⓒ lazy and content

    Ⓓ mean and afraid

4. Which of these will most likely happen in the future?

    Ⓐ Lupe will keep playing marbles.

    Ⓑ Lupe will become a great soccer player.

    Ⓒ Lupe will do poorly in school.

    Ⓓ Lupe will never play a sport again.

5. What is the theme of the story?

    Ⓐ It is hard to learn how to play marbles.

    Ⓑ Brothers and sisters should work together.

    Ⓒ Friendship is more important than winning.

    Ⓓ If you work hard, you can achieve a goal.

Vocabulary

▶ **Fill in the circle next to the correct definition of the underlined word.**

1. Lupe's aim was very <u>accurate</u>.
 Ⓐ lazy   Ⓒ difficult
 Ⓑ exact   Ⓓ large

2. She did exercises to <u>strengthen</u> her muscles.
 Ⓐ make stronger   Ⓒ wave
 Ⓑ lengthen   Ⓓ make smaller

3. Lupe's <u>opponent</u> was a good marbles player.
 Ⓐ family member   Ⓒ teammate
 Ⓑ coach   Ⓓ person who is against you

▶ **Choose the correct definition for the underlined multiple-meaning word.**

4. While she practiced, Lupe ate a snack for <u>energy</u>.
 Ⓐ electricity   Ⓒ strength
 Ⓑ rest   Ⓓ lunch

▶ **Choose the correct word from the word family.**

5. Lupe's family gave her a lot of _____.
 Ⓐ encourage   Ⓒ discourage
 Ⓑ courageous   Ⓓ encouragement

Short Answer

▶ **Use what you've read in this Workshop to answer the question below. Check your spelling and grammar.**

How would you describe Lupe Medrano's character?

_____

_____

_____

_____

Comprehension Focus
Cause and Effect

Taming Wild Beasts

Wild animals are at home in jungles, swamps, and open plains. But some wild animals live in zoos. Some even live in people's homes—as pets!

Are animals ever happy outside of the wild? Can wild beasts ever be tamed? Turn the page to find out.

VOCABULARY BUILDER

◎ Target Word ▶ Read the Target Words. Rate each one using the scale below.*	Meaning ▶ Read the Target Word meanings. Write in the missing ones.	Example ▶ Finish the Target Word examples below. Write in the missing ones.
capture cap•ture (verb) ① ② ③		I would like to capture . . .
enormous e•nor•mous (adjective) ① ② ③	very large	
fierce fierce (adjective) ① ② ③		A lion that's chasing its dinner is **fierce**.
habitat hab•i•tat (noun) ① ② ③	the natural environment of a plant or animal	
threat threat (noun) ① ② ③		Something that's a threat to me is . . .

*Rating Scale

① = I don't know it at all.

② = I've seen it before.

③ = I know it and use it.

The Big Idea

Write What is this article mainly about?

_____

_____

_____

VOCABULARY BUILDER

Target Word

remove

re•move (verb)

Rate it: ①   ②   ③

Meaning

_____

_____

Example

_____

_____

_____

React

Do you think the police were right to take away the tiger? Why or why not?

Ming the tiger was living in an apartment.

Pet Tiger Attack
New York Man Bitten by His Pet

October 4, 2003—Many people keep pets in their homes. But yesterday, Antoine Yates's pet was **removed** by the police. That's because the pet was a 450-pound tiger! Yates says the tiger is his best friend. But the police said it was a threat to the neighborhood.

Yates bought the tiger as a tiny cub. Tiger cubs are fuzzy and cute. So it's easy to see why someone might want one. Yates named his cub Ming. He fed Ming from a baby bottle. They wrestled and played together.

But soon, Ming grew to his enormous adult size. Playing with him became dangerous! One day, Ming chomped on Yates's arm and leg. Yates had to go to the hospital. But he didn't want to get Ming in trouble. So he told the doctors that a dog bit him. The doctors doubted Yates. He got nervous and ran off. That made the doctors call the police.

As a result, the police broke into Yates's home. They captured Ming. Then they transported him to a wild animal shelter. Yates misses his pet. But police and neighbors think Ming is where he belongs. **END**

Words to Know! **doubt** to not believe something

Cause and Effect

A **cause** is the reason something happens. An **effect** is the result of a cause.
To find cause and effect:

- Ask yourself "Why did it happen?" to find the cause.
- Ask yourself "What happened?" to find the effect.
- Look for signal words or phrases such as *because, so, as a result, therefore,* and *for this reason.*

▶ **Fill in this chart with the cause-and-effect relationships in "Pet Tiger Attack."**

Cause	Effect
_____ _____ _____ _____ _____	_____ _____ _____ _____ _____

Cause	Effect
_____ _____ _____ _____	_____ _____ _____ _____

WILD PETS

The Big Idea

Write What is this article mainly about?

_____

_____

_____

VOCABULARY BUILDER
 Target Word

concerned

con•cerned (adjective)

Rate it: ① ② ③

Meaning

_____

_____

Example

_____

_____

_____

React

What if *your* neighbor owned a pet alligator? How would you feel about that?

Do wild animals make good pets? One man thought so. But the law said no.

Many people like pets that are furry and cuddly. But John Boyko loves pets that are scaly and cold. He and his wife had three alligators!

The Gator Family

The Boykos got their first two alligators as babies. Later, they met a man who had an alligator he didn't want. The man was planning to kill the animal! So the Boykos rescued it.

The Boykos loved their alligators dearly. They played with their pets and took them for rides in the car. They even took the alligators to visit family. "We didn't have kids," said John Boyko. "We had gators."

John Boyko gets ready to take his pet alligators for a ride.

Afraid of Alligators

To John Boyko, his alligators were like any other pets. But his neighbors were **concerned**. In fact, they were terrified! Neighbor Margie Branca was afraid for her children. That's because alligators can be really fierce. "A dog bites you and backs off," Branca said. "An alligator bites you to eat you."

In time, some neighbors complained. As a result, the police came to the Boykos' house. They captured the alligators. They took the alligators away to a zoo.

The zookeeper said that the alligators were in good shape. He said that the Boykos "did a good job caring for the animals." John Boyko was mad! Like the zookeeper said, he knew that he was a good pet owner. So he felt he deserved to keep his pets. ➡

Words to Know!	**terrified** really scared

1. Underline ▶ Why did the Boykos have to rescue an alligator?

2. Write ▶ Why was neighbor Margie Branca terrified?

_____

_____

_____

_____

_____

3. Write ▶ What happened when the neighbors complained about the alligators?

_____

_____

_____

_____

_____

A boy plays with his wild pet snake.

Active Reading

Underline Why are some wild pets in danger?

VOCABULARY BUILDER
Target Word

legal
le•gal *(adjective)*

Rate it: ① ② ③

Meaning

_____

_____

Example

_____

_____

_____

React

Write Do you think people should be allowed to keep wild pets? Why or why not?

_____

_____

_____

_____

Pets in Danger

Should John Boyko and others be allowed to have wild pets? Some experts insist that almost nobody can handle a wild pet. Taking care of wild animals is costly—and hard. Often, they need expensive food and lots of exercise. And when they grow up, they can become a threat to their owners.

Because wild pets are so difficult, many owners abandon them. Then the pets end up in shelters, and the shelters get really crowded. As a result, some animals are even put to sleep.

Pets and the Law

States want to protect wild animals—by leaving them in the wild. That's why 19 states ban wild pets.

But wild pet owners say their pets should be **legal**. After all, this is America! People should have the right to choose the pets they like. Besides, many owners take good care of their wild pets.

What about John Boyko? He promises that *his* pets are totally safe and healthy. But his neighbors still don't believe him. So, for now, Boyko's alligators must stay at the zoo. ⟨END⟩

Words to Know! | **abandon** to leave something you are responsible for

Comprehension Focus
Cause and Effect
▶ **Fill in this chart with cause-and-effect relationships in "Wild Pets."**

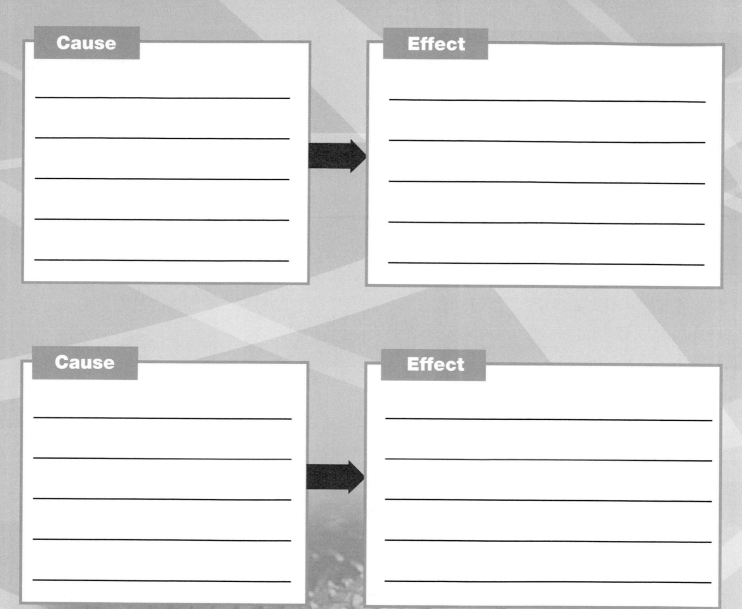

Cause

_____

_____

_____

_____

Effect

_____

_____

_____

_____

Cause

_____

_____

_____

_____

Effect

_____

_____

_____

_____

The Big Idea

Write ▶ What is this article mainly about?

_____

_____

_____

VOCABULARY BUILDER

 Target Word

range
range (noun)

Rate it: ①   ②   ③

Meaning

_____

_____

Example

_____

_____

_____

_____

 React

Would you like to live in a zoo? Yes or no? Explain your answer.

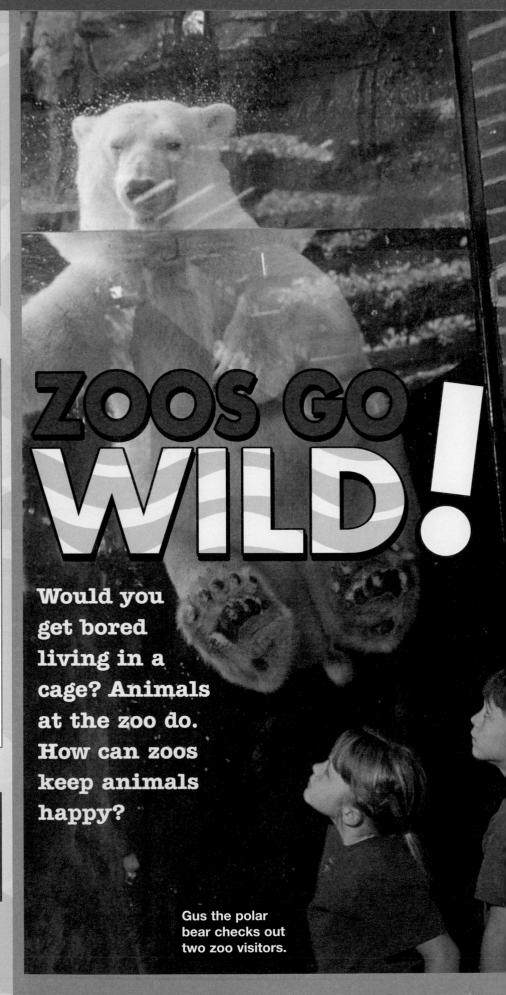

ZOOS GO WILD!

Would you get bored living in a cage? Animals at the zoo do. How can zoos keep animals happy?

Gus the polar bear checks out two zoo visitors.

The Bored Bear

Today, Gus the polar bear is a star. He lives at the Central Park Zoo in New York City. Kids love to come watch him swim and play. But Gus wasn't always so much fun. Back in 1994, he had a problem. He would swim laps for hours without stopping. Gus wasn't sick. He wasn't losing his mind, either. Gus did laps because he was so *bored*!

Gus was not alone. Many zoo animals are bored and unhappy. That's because they prefer the wild. In the wild, animals roam in packs. They hunt, play, and fight. In other words, they have things to do.

Home on the Range

Zoo experts are aware of this problem. They study animals' lives in the wild. They try to figure out what zoo animals are missing. Often, animals that are unhappy in a zoo have large "home **ranges**" in the wild. A home range is the area where a wild animal lives and roams.

Polar bears have huge home ranges. In the wild, they roam up to 31,000 miles a year. They also hunt for seals on the ice. Zoo cages are tiny compared to the wild. As a result, a polar bear like Gus gets restless. He has nowhere to roam and no seals to hunt.

Lions and tigers also have big home ranges. In the wild, they roam around and hunt for smaller animals. So, like polar bears, they get bored in the zoo.

Other animals do better in zoos. Snow leopards have small home ranges. Because of this, they are less bored by zoo life. ➡

Words to Know! **roam** to travel

1. Underline ▶ Find the sentence that tells why Gus swam laps for hours.

2. Write ▶ Why don't polar bears do well in zoos?

_____

_____

_____

3. Write ▶ Why are snow leopards happier in zoos?

_____

_____

_____

Review:
Problem and Solution

Circle ▶ Find the sentence that describes the main problem with putting polar bears in cages.

Active Reading

 Star ▶ What animal has a zoo home built like the Congo Forest?

VOCABULARY BUILDER

 Target Word

exhibit

ex•hib•it *(noun)*

Rate it: ① ② ③

Meaning

_____

_____

Example

_____

_____

_____

 React

Write ▶ What zoo animal would you like to learn more about? Tell why.

_____

_____

_____

_____

_____

Gus's New Home

Gus's zookeepers wanted to help him out. So they rebuilt his home. Now his **exhibit** is more like his natural habitat. His tank is a fake river. And Gus has a snow bank to keep himself cool.

The zookeepers have also made Gus's life more interesting. Gus loves to eat fish. In the old days, the zoo just gave it to him. But now Gus has to work for his dinner. The zoo freezes his fish in ice. Then, they bury it in some gravel. Gus has to find it before he can eat it. He also has to remove the fish from the ice.

Gus's new home is working out well. He swims laps less often now. He doesn't seem so bored. And kids love to visit him.

 TEXT FEATURE Reading a Map

Bronx Zoo Congo Gorilla Forest

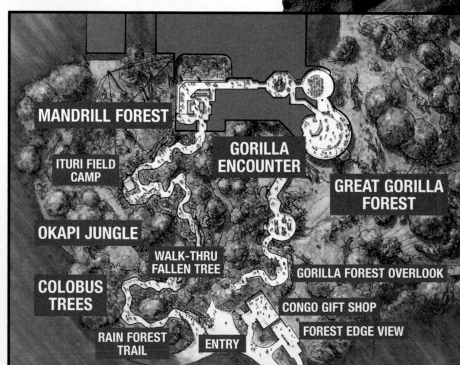

MANDRILL FOREST

ITURI FIELD CAMP

GORILLA ENCOUNTER

GREAT GORILLA FOREST

OKAPI JUNGLE

WALK-THRU FALLEN TREE

GORILLA FOREST OVERLOOK

COLOBUS TREES

CONGO GIFT SHOP

FOREST EDGE VIEW

RAIN FOREST TRAIL

ENTRY

No More Bars

Gus isn't the only animal with a new cage. Today, many zoos are "going wild."

The Bronx Zoo in New York spent seven years making a better home for gorillas. The new exhibit was built to seem like the Congo forest. As a result, the gorillas are surrounded by trees and waterfalls. From inside a glass tunnel, visitors can see a band of gorillas at play.

At the San Diego Zoo, enormous elephants, tall giraffes, and fierce rhinos roam freely in a huge park. People travel through it on a train. It feels like an African safari!

Zoos are getting good results from their new exhibits. The animals seem happier. And more people visit. Zoos are now more fun for everyone. END

Words to Know!	**safari** a trip taken to see large animals

A map is a detailed plan of a place. It shows where things are in relation to each other.

1. Where do you think the gorillas live?

Ⓐ Congo Gift Shop
Ⓑ Great Gorilla Forest
Ⓒ Okapi Jungle
Ⓓ Entry

2. What is between the Okapi Jungle and the Mandrill Forest?

Ⓐ the Ituri Field Camp
Ⓑ the Colobus Trees
Ⓒ the Walk-Thru Fallen Tree
Ⓓ the Congo Gift Shop

3. Which place on the map would you most like to see?

_____

_____

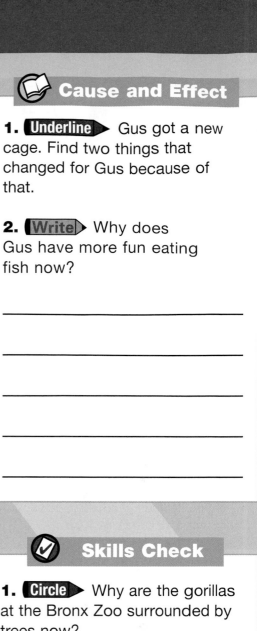

Cause and Effect

1. **Underline** Gus got a new cage. Find two things that changed for Gus because of that.

2. **Write** Why does Gus have more fun eating fish now?

_____

_____

_____

_____

_____

Skills Check

1. **Circle** Why are the gorillas at the Bronx Zoo surrounded by trees now?

2. **Write** What are two effects of new zoo designs?

• _____

_____

_____

• _____

_____

_____

Take the WORD CHALLENGE

START

1 **Check one.** Which expression makes someone look the most fierce?

☐ a smile ☐ a frown

☐ a snarl ☐ a laugh

❖❖❖❖❖❖❖❖

2 **Fill in.** Name three things that are part of your habitat at home.

- _____

- _____

- _____

There is a lot of stuff in this **habitat!**

3 **Multiple-Meaning Words**
Multiple-meaning words are words that have more than one meaning. For example, a *bat* is a small mammal that flies at night. But a *bat* is also what a baseball player uses to hit baseballs.

Look up the word *range* in the glossary. Then, check the definitions that go with *range*.

☐ The area where an animal lives and roams

☐ A line of mountains

☐ Strange and unusual things in a movie

☐ A variety of a group of things

4 **Rate them.** Which threats are you concerned about? Write **NC** for not concerned. Write **C** for concerned.

_____ an earthquake   _____ a shark attack

_____ lightning   _____ aliens from outer space

_____ a mean neighbor   _____ being chased by a lion

❖❖❖❖❖❖❖❖❖❖❖❖❖❖❖

5 **Fill in the blanks.**
Finish each sentence below.

A police officer captures _____ .

A dogcatcher captures _____ .

A fisherman captures _____ .

6

Rate them. These are possible slogans for a new ice cream store. Rate them from 1 to 4.

1 = the worst
4 = the best

_____ "We serve small scoops of ice cream on enormous cones!"

_____ "We sell enormous scoops of ice cream for a small price!"

_____ "We sell small scoops of ice cream at enormous prices!"

_____ "We sell enormous scoops of ice cream at enormous prices!"

7

Fill in. Complete this sentence with habitats and exhibits.

At the Bronx Zoo, visitors see animals

in _____ that are

a lot like the animals' natural

_____ .

8

> I **flip** through the air with ease! A minute ago, I **flipped** three times.

Verb Endings

A **verb ending** can be added to a verb to show when an action takes place. To show that an action happened in the past, you can often add -ed. To show that an action happens in the present, you can often add -ing.

Yesterday, I *played.*   Today, I am *playing.*

Add the verb. Use the correct verb ending.

1. Last week, we _____ a lost bird. (capture)

2. No, I'm not done yet. I'm _____ my homework right now! (finish)

3. After they _____ the cast from my arm, I was able to play baseball again. (remove)

9

Think about it. Decide if each animal should be legal or not legal to own as a pet.

	should be legal	should not be legal
polar bear	☐	☐
dolphin	☐	☐
rat	☐	☐
duck	☐	☐

10

Fill in. Tell what would happen if . . .

• one tire was removed from a car?

_____

• one whisker was removed from a sleeping tiger?

_____

• all the teeth were removed from your mouth?

_____

FINISH   Taming Wild Beasts 177

Writing Focus

Narrative Paragraph

A **narrative paragraph** tells a story about an event.

▶ **Read Gwen's narrative paragraph about a scary experience she had with a dog.**

Student Model

My Escape From Boo the Dog

by Gwen Stamper

When I was in the third grade, my sister and I were chased by a fierce, enormous dog named Boo. First, we tried to avoid Boo by walking quickly past his yard. Boo barked at us and jumped over his fence! Then he began chasing us! We ran like scared rabbits to escape Boo. Finally, we made it home to our front door just before he caught up with us. My mom called Boo's owner and told her to take him away. In the end, we were safe, but we never wanted to see Boo again.

Parts of a Narrative Paragraph

▶ **Find these parts of Gwen's narrative paragraph.**

1. Underline the sentence that tells about the **event**.
2. Check three **details** that explain the event.
3. Number the details in the **time order** they happened.
4. Circle the **linking words** that connect the details.
5. Put a star by the sentence that **sums up** the event and tells the writer's feelings about it.

Brainstorm

▶ Read the writing prompt in the middle of the idea web. Then, use the boxes to help you brainstorm your ideas.

Funny Experiences

Scary Experiences

Writing Prompt:
What interesting experience have you had with an animal?

Weird Experiences

Sad Experiences

Plan Your Paragraph

Writing Prompt: What interesting experience have you had with an animal?

▶ **Use this chart to plan your paragraph.**

Word Choices

_____

_____

_____

_____

_____

Event

- *When I was . . .*
- *The scariest day of my life was when . . .*
- *Once, when I was . . .*

First Detail

- *First, . . .*
- *One day, . . .*
- *The story began when . . .*

Second Detail

- *Then, . . .*
- *The very next minute . . .*
- *Two days later, . . .*

Third Detail

- *Finally, . . .*
- *Before long, . . .*
- *Soon, . . .*

Ending

- *In the end, . . .*
- *What this all means to me . . .*
- *I'm happy to say . . .*

Write Your Paragraph

▶ Use the writing frame to write a first draft of your paragraph.

_____

(title)

When I was _____

_____

_____

First, _____

_____

_____

Then, _____

_____

_____

_____

Finally, _____

_____

_____

_____

In the end, _____

_____

_____

_____

Revise

▶ Rate your paragraph. Then have a writing partner rate it.

Scoring Guide			
weak	okay	good	strong
1	2	3	4

1. Does the beginning tell about the **event**?

Self	1	2	3	4
Partner	1	2	3	4

2. Are there **details** that explain the event?

Self	1	2	3	4
Partner	1	2	3	4

3. Are the details written in the **time order** they happened?

Self	1	2	3	4
Partner	1	2	3	4

4. Do **linking words** connect the details?

Self	1	2	3	4
Partner	1	2	3	4

5. Does the ending **sum up** the event and tell the writer's feelings about it?

Self	1	2	3	4
Partner	1	2	3	4

▶ Now revise your paragraph to make it stronger.

Grammar USING SUBJECT AND OBJECT PRONOUNS

A **pronoun** is a word that takes the place of a noun in a sentence.

- Use a subject pronoun in the subject of a sentence.
- Use an object pronoun after a verb or after a word such as *for* or *to*.

Example

Subject Pronoun	Object Pronoun
I have a pet turtle.	My turtle Myrtle likes me.
We found Myrtle in the yard.	Myrtle crawled right up to us.
She eats lettuce for dinner.	Once, I gave a dead fly to her.

▶ **Circle the correct pronoun. Write whether it is a subject or object pronoun.**

1. [(I) Me] gave a pet snake to my friend.   *subject*

2. Jamal named [he him] Fangs.   _____

3. [Them They] were always together.   _____

4. One day, Fangs bit [I me] on the thumb.   _____

5. Jamal's mom gave [he him] to a pet store.   _____

6. Jamal and [I me] plan to visit Fangs.   _____

▶ **Rewrite these sentences using a pronoun for the underlined words.**

7. <u>Fangs</u> grew bigger and bigger!

_____

8. Finally, <u>Jamal and I</u> saw a family buy Fangs.

_____

9. We followed <u>the family</u> out of the store.

_____

10. <u>Jamal</u> was sad when the family drove away.

_____

 Edit ▶ *Take a close look at each of the sentences in your draft on page 181. Do they all use subject and object pronouns correctly? Fix the ones that don't.*

Usage AVOIDING DOUBLE NEGATIVES

Negatives are words that mean *no* or *not*.

- Use only one negative word to express a single negative idea.
- It is incorrect to use two negatives to express a negative idea.

Example

Correct	Incorrect
Tigers should never be pets.	Tigers shouldn't never be pets.
The alligator didn't eat anything.	The alligator didn't eat nothing.

▶ **Find and correct five errors in this paragraph.**

Check and Correct
- ❑ Circle two spelling errors and correct them.
- ❑ Underline one subject-object pronoun error and correct it.
- ❑ Correct two double-negative errors.

Student Model

Last year, a feirce dog attacked my rabbits. First, he jumped over my fence. He barked at me. Next, him tried to break into my rabbits' cage. Then, I threw a stick at him. But I didn't not hit him. Finaly, the dog ran away. I did not never see him again. I gave my bunnies a hug. In conclusion, I saved them from disaster. They were lucky!

Edit *Look at the sentences in your draft on page 181. Are they free of double negatives? Fix the ones that have double negatives.*

Final Draft/Present

▶ **Write a final draft of your paragraph on paper or the computer. Check it again and correct any errors before you present it.**

Careers

Veterinary Technician

Meet Maura Mayo. She works with a veterinarian to take care of animals. She gives them shots and takes X-rays. She also explains pet care instructions to owners. "It's exciting to see the animals get well after they've been in for treatment," Maura says. "I love watching their owners come to bring them home. They are so happy!"

Name: Maura Mayo

Hometown: Fairfield, Connecticut

Job: Veterinary Technician for Engelberg Kristy Animal Hospital

Duties:
- preps animals for surgery
- gives them medications
- explains pet care instructions

Skills:
- knowledge of health and medicine
- ability to lift and restrain animals
- ability to stay calm during emergencies
- communicating with pet owners

Similar Jobs:
- pet groomer
- veterinarian
- dog walker

Pay: $7 to $24 per hour, depending on experience

Education: Veterinary Technician Certificate required. You can study for this at a community college.

Maura gives a dog a shot.

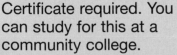

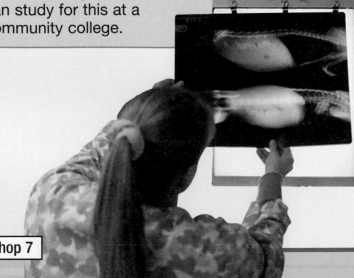

Ask Yourself

1. **Underline** Which of the similar jobs would you be best at?

2. **Circle** Find the pay rate for this job.

3. **Check** How much do you want this job?

   ☐ I don't want it.

   ☐ I might want it.

   ☐ I really want it.

Following Pet Care Directions

Maura might use a flyer like the one below to help a new pet owner understand pet care. The flyer below is about caring for a dog. Read it. Then answer the questions to the right.

Take Care of Your Dog

DOG SUPPLIES

- Buy the following items before you bring your dog home:
  - ☐ food   ☐ shampoo   ☐ bowls
  - ☐ leash   ☐ collar   ☐ chewing toys
  - ☐ brush   ☐ comb

FEEDING

- Puppies eight to twelve weeks old need four meals a day.
- Puppies three to six months old need three meals a day.
- Puppies six months to one year old need two meals a day.
- Older dogs need only one meal a day.
- Wash food and water bowls regularly.

EXERCISE

- Every dog needs daily exercise.

HOUSING

- A dog's bed should be in a warm, quiet place.
- Puppies should not sleep on the floor.

▶ **Fill in the circle next to the correct answer.**

1. What section tells you what things you need to buy for a dog?
   - Ⓐ Feeding
   - Ⓑ Exercise
   - Ⓒ Dog Supplies
   - Ⓓ Housing

2. Do all dogs need daily exercise?
   - Ⓐ yes
   - Ⓑ no
   - Ⓒ only some breeds
   - Ⓓ only if they eat too much

3. How often should you feed a ten-month-old puppy?
   - Ⓐ eight times a day
   - Ⓑ once a day
   - Ⓒ twice a day
   - Ⓓ four times a day

4. What is one supply you need to care for a dog?
   - Ⓐ a big yard
   - Ⓑ a dog bath
   - Ⓒ a leash
   - Ⓓ a chain-link fence

5. Where should dogs sleep?
   - Ⓐ somewhere wet and cold
   - Ⓑ in the street
   - Ⓒ in a warm, quiet place
   - Ⓓ in the yard

Comprehension

▶ **Choose the best answer to each question. Fill in the bubble.**

1. Ming the tiger was taken away from Antoine Yates because _____.

   Ⓐ he had eaten a neighbor's dog

   Ⓑ the police found out that Ming had bitten Yates

   Ⓒ the police found out that Ming had bitten a veterinarian

   Ⓓ he was growling in the night

> **Here's a Tip!**
> Read over your answers carefully. Double-check that you filled in the answers in the correct places.

2. Why do most wild animal pets get abandoned at shelters?

   Ⓐ They are too boring for owners to enjoy them.

   Ⓑ They escape from owners' homes and are caught by police.

   Ⓒ They need expensive food and can become dangerous.

   Ⓓ Owners feel sorry for them and want them to go back to the wild.

3. Why do some people think that wild pets should be outlawed?

   Ⓐ They are too big.

   Ⓑ They are too dangerous.

   Ⓒ They are too pretty.

   Ⓓ They are too unhappy.

4. According to a new study, what animals do poorly in zoos?

   Ⓐ animals with large home ranges

   Ⓑ polar bears

   Ⓒ lions and tigers

   Ⓓ all of the above

5. How are some zoos changing?

   Ⓐ They are making the animals do more tricks.

   Ⓑ They are making animal cages smaller.

   Ⓒ They are making animals' exhibits more like the wild.

   Ⓓ They are closing down because people hate zoos.

Vocabulary

▶ **Choose the answer that best defines the underlined word.**

1. Wild pets can be a <u>threat</u> to their owners.
- Ⓐ a friend
- Ⓒ a joy
- Ⓑ a punishment
- Ⓓ a danger

2. In their home <u>habitat</u>, polar bears are used to roaming far distances.
- Ⓐ family group that includes several generations
- Ⓒ zoo cages
- Ⓑ the natural environment of a plant or animal
- Ⓓ state

3. <u>Enormous</u> elephants seem peaceful, but when attacked, they can be <u>fierce</u>.
- Ⓐ very large; wild and violent
- Ⓒ big-eared; loud
- Ⓑ baby; unhappy
- Ⓓ pet; ugly

▶ **Mark the correct form of *capture* in the following sentence.**

4. The police _____ the bear that had attacked the campers.
- Ⓐ capture
- Ⓒ captured
- Ⓑ capturing
- Ⓓ capturer

▶ **Choose the correct definition for *range* as it's used in this sentence.**

5. The ice-cream store offers a <u>range</u> of flavors.
- Ⓐ area where an animal lives and roams
- Ⓒ least amount
- Ⓑ a variety of a group of things
- Ⓓ a line of mountains

Short Answer

▶ **Use what you've read in this Workshop to answer the questions below. Check your spelling and grammar.**

Do you think people should be allowed to have wild pets in your community? Explain your answer.

_____

_____

_____

Workshop 8
Nonfiction

Comprehension Focus
Compare and Contrast

READINGS
1 Food Fight: Chefs Vs. Kids >> Newspaper Article
2 Bugs Vs. Burgers >> Magazine Article
3 You Are What You Eat >> Health Science Feature

FOOD
the **Good,**
the **Bad,**
and the **GROSS**

Some foods are bad for us. Some foods are good for us. And some foods are just plain gross! Get ready to take a food tour that includes all three.

You'll sample school cafeteria menus, compare the tastes of bugs and burgers, and finish up with tips about a healthy diet and exercise. Hold on to your stomach, and get ready to read!

VOCABULARY BUILDER

◎ Target Word ► Read the Target Words. Rate each one using the scale below.*	Meaning ► Read the Target Word meanings. Write in the missing ones.	Example ► Finish the Target Word examples below. Write in the missing ones.
appeal ap•peal (verb) ① ② ③		Foods that appeal to me are . . .
nutritious nu•tri•tious (adjective) ① ② ③	healthy	
prefer pre•fer (verb) ① ② ③		For dessert, I prefer . . . more than . . .
satisfy sat•is•fy (verb) ① ② ③	to please someone by doing enough or giving enough	
variety va•ri•e•ty (noun) ① ② ③		Ice cream comes in a **variety** of flavors.

*Rating Scale
①= I don't know it at all.
②= I've seen it before.
③= I know it and use it.

The Big Idea

Write What is this article mainly about?

_____

_____

_____

VOCABULARY BUILDER

Target Word

habit
hab•it (noun)

Rate it: ① ② ③

Meaning

_____

_____

Example

_____

_____

_____

_____

React

How would you rate your school lunches? What would make your school lunches better?

FOOD FIGHT: Chefs Vs. Kids

Kids check out what's for lunch.

School Chefs and Students Face Off

SEPTEMBER, 2005—This year, there's a new lunch menu in New York City schools. New chefs want to offer healthier options. But they are off to a rough start. Many kids have a **habit** of eating only junk food.

So, what's for lunch? Both chefs and kids love burgers. Chefs serve up nutritious veggie burgers. But kids don't bite. They want meat burgers. The veggie burgers have a "weird flavor," one kid says.

Chefs know that side dishes can make or break a meal. Kids think so, too. So, chefs offer baked fries and vegetables. However, kids prefer *fried* fries. One student thinks vegetables are not very appealing. "They don't taste good," she says.

Chefs like to provide dessert. Kids also want dessert. That's why chefs offer fruit. Does that work? No! Instead of trying a pear, kids select cookies from vending machines. Chefs keep trying. But nothing is working! How can they satisfy kids? The girl who hates veggies has an idea. "You have to hide the vegetables where I can't see them," she says. END

Words to Know! **select** choose

Comprehension Focus

Compare and Contrast

When you **compare**, you tell how two things are the same. When you **contrast**, you tell how they are different. To compare and contrast:

• Ask yourself how two things are the same. Look for signal words such as *both*, *too*, *also*, and *in addition*.

• Ask yourself how two things are different. Look for signal words such as *but*, *rather than*, *however*, *unlike*, and *instead*.

▶ Fill in this chart to compare and contrast what the school chefs want to serve and what the students want to eat.

School Chefs   Students

Different	Same	Different
1. Burgers	**1. Burgers**	**1. Burgers**
_____	Both groups think burgers	_____
_____	are a good main course.	_____
2. Side Dishes	**2. Side Dishes**	**2. Side Dishes**
_____	Both groups want side	_____
_____	dishes to be part of lunch.	_____
3. Desserts	**3. Desserts**	**3. Desserts**
_____	Both groups know that	_____
_____	kids love dessert.	_____

The Big Idea

Write What is this article mainly about?

_____

_____

_____

VOCABULARY BUILDER

 Target Word

average
av•er•age (adjective)

Rate it: ① ② ③

Meaning

_____

_____

Example

_____

_____

_____

 React

What is the grossest thing you've ever eaten? What made it gross?

This Thai woman is selling roasted grasshoppers in a market.

Bugs Vs. Burgers

Are bugs totally gross to eat? Read the facts—you may change your mind!

The World Loves Bugs

Most people think bugs are just delicious. In fact, 80 percent of people around the world eat bugs. Families in Venezuela roast tarantulas over fires. In South Africa, people go buggy over fried termites. In Japan, diners may spend as much as $40 on one plate of baby flies!

Most Americans, however, think bugs are gross. The only Americans you might see eating bugs are those trying to win a million dollars on TV. The **average** American would much rather eat a juicy burger than a juicy bug!

Are bugs *really* disgusting? Your answer probably depends on what you're used to eating. That's how most people decide what's good and what's gross. But there's more to the story. How nutritious are bugs, compared to burgers? How hard is it to grow and cook bugs? And do burgers really win the taste test?

Here's to Your Health

Doctors say that a diet high in protein and low in fat is best for people. Following this kind of diet can prevent heart disease or diabetes.

The average beef burger is packed with protein! A burger with all the fixings has about 25 grams of protein. Burgers also have 34 grams of fat.

How do bugs compare? Like burgers, bugs are packed with protein. A dinner of grasshoppers has about 21 grams of protein. Unlike burgers, bugs have very little fat. That dinner of grasshoppers has only 6 grams of fat. For a nutritious meal, bugs win out over beef burgers. ➡

Words to Know! **percent** part of a whole

Compare and Contrast

1. **Write** How are Americans different from 80 percent of the world?

_____

_____

_____

_____

_____

2. **Underline** Find one similarity between bugs and burgers.

3. **Circle** Find one difference between bugs and burgers.

Active Reading

Star What do some bugs taste like?

VOCABULARY BUILDER
Target Word

adjust

ad•just (verb)

Rate it: ① ② ③

Meaning

_____

_____

Example

_____

_____

_____

React

Write If a friend served you a bug sandwich, would you taste it? Why or why not?

_____

_____

_____

_____

Fast Food

Fried grasshoppers can be a yummy treat!

There are also big differences between how we get bugs and beef. Bugs and cows can both be raised on farms. Crickets are raised in just six weeks. Farmers need only 100 pounds of feed to raise 45 pounds of crickets. However, cows take two years to raise. To get 45 pounds of beef, farmers must use a whopping 1,125 pounds of feed. That's ten times as much feed as crickets need.

Burger restaurants are much easier for Americans to find than bug stands. You can buy a burger in any fast food restaurant. But bugs can only be found in specialty stores and on the Web.

At home, both bugs and burgers are easy to cook. Burgers are usually fried up in a pan. Bugs can be made this way, too. It's not a complex process to prepare them. Just add salt, ketchup, and enjoy!

The Taste Test

Burgers taste meaty and salty—flavors that appeal to most Americans. Bug-eaters say bugs are yummy, too. Unlike burgers, bugs come in a variety of flavors. Most bugs are nice and crunchy on the outside—like popcorn! A type of Mexican stinkbug has a cinnamon flavor.

Bugs are nutritious, cheap, and yummy. Will Americans **adjust** their tastes and learn to love them? We'll have to wait and see.

So, the next time you suffer from a bug bite, remember—it might be time to bite back! **END**

Words to Know! **complex** with many parts

Compare and Contrast

▶ Fill in this chart to compare and contrast bugs and burgers, using the sections "Fast Food" and "The Taste Test."

Bugs

Different

1. _____

_____

_____

2. _____

_____

_____

3. _____

_____

Same

1. _____

_____

_____

2. _____

_____

_____

3. _____

Burgers

Different

1. _____

_____

_____

2. _____

_____

_____

3. _____

_____

You Are What You EAT

Zac Garcia prepares a salad at home.

The Big Idea

 Write What is this article mainly about?

_____

_____

_____

VOCABULARY BUILDER

 Target Word

neglect

ne•glect (verb)

Rate it: ① ② ③

Meaning

_____

_____

Example

_____

_____

_____

React

Which of the exercises on page 197 would you most want to do? Explain why.

Kids today aren't very healthy. It's time to do something about it—before it's too late.

Getting Healthy

Sixth-grader Zac Garcia wasn't feeling so good. On an average day, he was tired. He didn't have much energy. So, he decided to improve his health. First, he adjusted his diet. He ate larger portions of fruits and vegetables. He also ate nutritious snacks.

Then, Zac adjusted his exercise habits. He had always been active. But he wanted to do even more. He started riding his bike more often. He started walking more.

Within six months, Zac had lost 10 pounds. These days, he has less fat and more muscle. He also has more energy. "I used to run a mile in 10.5 minutes. Now I run a mile in only 9.5," he said.

Get Physical

Many American kids **neglect** to exercise enough. The average kid spends only 14 minutes a day working out. Being active can be a challenge. But it can also be fun. Zac chose biking and walking to get active. But there are a variety of ways to get exercise. You can burn 150 calories with any of these activities:

- Shoot hoops for 30 minutes
- Wash and wax a car for 45–60 minutes
- Rake leaves for 30 minutes
- Walk 2 miles in 30 minutes
- Play touch football for 45 minutes
- Wheel self in a wheelchair for 30–40 minutes
- In-line skate for 20–25 minutes

Words to Know! **portion** an amount of food for one person

Compare and Contrast

1. **Underline** Find the sentence that contrasts how Zac feels now with how he felt before.

2. **Write** Contrast the different activities listed. Which takes the longest?

_____

_____

3. **Write** Which activity takes the least amount of time?

_____

_____

Review: Cause and Effect

Write What effect did Zac's new habits have on his running speed?

_____

_____

_____

Active Reading

Star What diseases can people get from a high-fat diet?

VOCABULARY BUILDER

◎ **Target Word**

necessity

ne•ces•si•ty
(noun)
Rate it: ① ② ③

Meaning

_____

_____

Example

_____

_____

_____

_____

! React

Write What snack do you like the most? Is it healthy?

_____

_____

_____

_____

_____

Burgers and Fries

Not every kid is as healthy as Zac. In fact, in 2005, about 15 percent of American kids ages 6–18 were overweight. That's more kids than ever before. Back in 1980, for example, only 5.7 percent of children were overweight.

What's going on? Experts say many American kids prefer fast food to more healthy options. It's a favorite source for food. In 2002, Americans spent $110 billion on fast food. That's more than they spent on movies, books, magazines, videos, and music—combined! The average American ate three burgers and four orders of french fries per week.

The Science Behind the Diet

What's wrong with a fast food diet? It may satisfy your taste buds. However, it's not so great for your health. Fast food comes mostly from two food groups—meat and fat. The Food Guide Pyramid (at right) shows how much to eat from each group.

Down at the bottom are the foods we need most. Grains should be a big part of every diet. Fruits and vegetables should also be eaten often. Fat is at the top, with meat just below it. They are a **necessity**, too. But we should eat them only in small amounts.

When people eat too much fat, their bodies suffer. Fat in your diet can lead to weight gain. That can lead to diabetes, heart disease, and even arthritis.

If you want to be healthy, check out the Food Guide Pyramid. How do your eating habits compare? Then, ask your doctor about a good diet for you. Get started with good eating habits—and you'll probably keep them for life. ⟨END⟩

Words to Know! **source** where something comes from

The Food Guide Pyramid

The small part at the top is for fats, oils, and sweets. You should eat small amounts of these.

The second level is for dairy products and protein. You should eat 3 servings of low-fat or fat-free dairy a day. You should eat 2 to 4 servings of protein a day.

The third level is for fruits and vegetables. You should eat 2 to 4 fruits each day, and 4 to 6 servings of vegetables.

The bottom level is for grains. You need 5 to 8 servings every day.

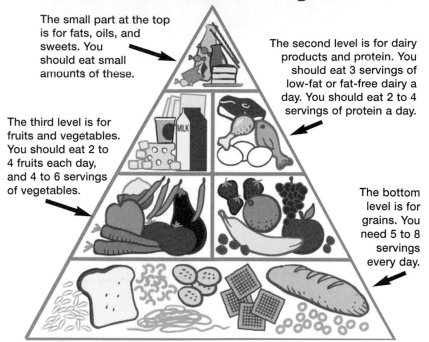

A diagram is a drawing that explains something.

1. Which food group should you eat the most servings of daily?

   Ⓐ fruits   Ⓑ fats   Ⓒ grains   Ⓓ dairy

2. How many servings of protein should you eat every day?

   Ⓐ 2 to 4   Ⓑ 4 to 6   Ⓒ 2 to 3   Ⓓ 8 to 10

3. Looking at the chart, are there any groups from which you don't eat enough servings? Explain.

   _____

   _____

📖 Compare and Contrast

1. **Underline** ▶ Find the paragraph that contrasts kids from 1980 with kids from 2005.

2. **Circle** ▶ How much did Americans spend on fast food, compared to other items?

✓ Skills Check

1. **Circle** ▶ How are fruits and vegetables similar to grains, according to the food pyramid?

2. **Write** ▶ How much fat should you eat, contrasted with fruits, vegetables, and meat?

   _____

   _____

   _____

Take the WORD CHALLENGE

START

1 Rate them. Which activity appeals to you most? Which appeals to you least?

1 = least appealing
4 = most appealing

____ riding a roller coaster

____ eating a worm

____ dying your hair green

____ giving a class report

2 Circle them. Read the two items in each row. Circle the one you prefer.

cats	OR	dogs
football	OR	basketball
TV	OR	movies
drawing	OR	reading

3 Synonyms

Synonyms are words that have similar meanings. Examples are *smart* and *clever*, or *boring* and *dull*.

Match each word below to its synonym.

disease	fun
similar	sickness
enjoyable	giant
huge	alike

It's so cold outside, I'd better **adjust** my outfit. I'll **change** into a sweater.

4 Decide. Which foods below do you think are nutritious? Check them. Then circle the foods that you would want to eat.

☐ grasshoppers   ☐ fruit salad   ☐ bubble gum

☐ fish-head soup   ☐ veggie burgers   ☐ ice cream

☐ vegetable soup   ☐ hamburgers   ☐ jelly beans

★ ★ ★ ★ ★ ★

5 Check. Which of the things below do you sometimes neglect? Write **SN** for sometimes neglect, or **NN** for never neglect.

____ your friends   ____ your pet

____ your chores   ____ watching TV

____ your homework   ____ exercising

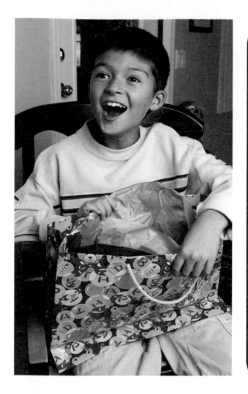

6 Analyze.
Name three things you think are necessities for having a good birthday party.

- _____
- _____
- _____

★ ★ ★ ★

7 Evaluate.
Which of these statements might you make if you were *really* satisfied with something?

☐ "Well, it's OK . . . I guess."

☐ "Great! Perfect! I love it!"

☐ "This could be better."

8 Suffixes
A **suffix** is a letter or group of letters added to the end of a word. A suffix changes the meaning or part of speech of a word. The suffix *-able* changes a verb to an adjective.

Fill in. Change these verbs to adjectives by adding the suffix *-able.*

adjust   _____

read   _____

believe   _____

enjoy   _____

9 Fill in.
Write either habits or variety in the first two blanks. Fill in the third blank with your own idea.

My little sister has a _____ of bad _____, like picking her nose and chewing smelly bubble gum. But the worst thing she does is _____ _____.

My dog may not be **cute,** but he is very **lovable.**

10 Think.
Name three things you do on an average school night.

- _____
  _____
- _____
- _____

FINISH

Writing Focus
Descriptive Paragraph

A descriptive paragraph describes a person, place, or thing by offering important details.

▶ **Read Marguerite's descriptive paragraph about her favorite meal.**

Student Model

> The Amazing Quesadillas
> by Marguerite Arroyo
>
> My favorite food is my grandma's amazing quesadillas. I know she is making them when I hear the sizzle of a quesadilla cooking in a pan. When the tasty brown tortilla is done, my grandma serves it with a splatter of red salsa on top. It looks so appealing. Also, the smell of the hot cheese and spicy salsa makes my mouth water! As I cut into the quesadilla, I can feel the crunchy outside and the soft inside. Finally, it's time to taste it. The rich, spicy flavors always satisfy me. My grandma's amazing quesadillas will always be my favorite dish.

Parts of a Descriptive Paragraph

▶ **Find these parts of Marguerite's descriptive paragraph.**

1. Underline the sentence that tells **what is being described**.
2. Check three sentences with **descriptive details**.
3. Put a box around the descriptive detail you think is most **interesting**.
4. Circle the **linking words** that connect the details.
5. Put a star beside the sentence that **sums up** the description and tells the writer's **feelings** about it.

Brainstorm

▶ Read the writing prompt in the middle of the idea web. Then use the boxes to help you brainstorm your ideas.

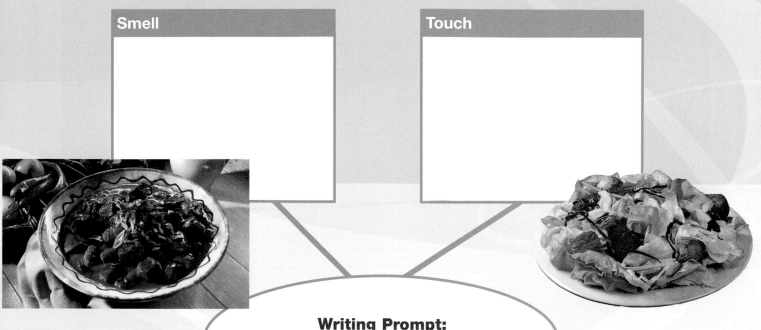

Smell

Touch

Writing Prompt:
Describe your favorite food or meal.

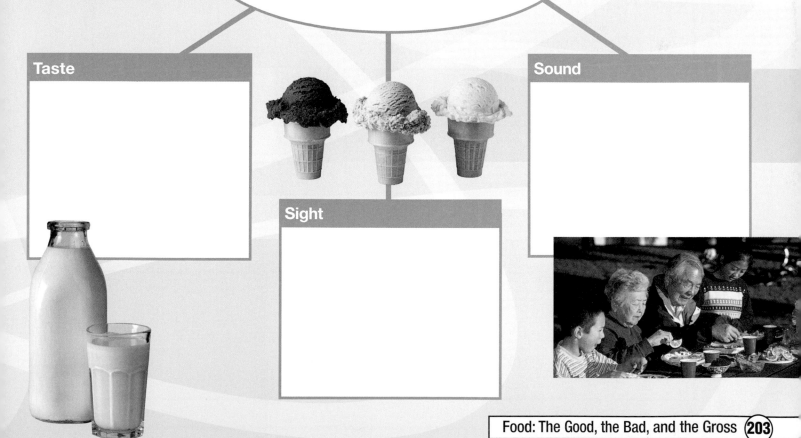

Taste

Sound

Sight

Plan Your Paragraph

Writing Prompt: Describe your favorite food or meal.

▶ Use this chart to plan and organize your paragraph.

Word Choices

_____

_____

_____

_____

_____

Topic Sentence

- *My favorite food . . .*

- *If I could have anything to eat . . .*

- *I've always loved . . .*

Descriptive Detail

- *I know he/she is making it when I hear . . .*

- *The flavor of . . .*

- *The smell of . . .*

Descriptive Detail

- *When the tasty . . .*

- *This dish looks . . .*

- *Whenever I eat it . . .*

Descriptive Detail

- *It looks . . .*

- *The taste of . . .*

- *When I see all the . . .*

Conclusion

- *_____ will always be . . .*

- *After eating all that, . . .*

- *Just thinking about . . .*

Write Your Paragraph

▶ Use this writing frame to write a first draft of your paragraph.

_____
(title)

My favorite food _____

_____

_____

I know _____

_____

_____

When the tasty _____

_____

_____

_____

It looks _____

_____

_____

_____

_____ will always be _____

_____

_____

_____

Revise

▶ **Rate your paragraph. Then have a writing partner rate it.**

Scoring Guide			
weak	okay	good	strong
1	2	3	4

1. Does the beginning clearly state **what is being described**?

Self   1 2 3 4

Partner 1 2 3 4

2. Do the sentences contain **descriptive details**?

Self   1 2 3 4

Partner 1 2 3 4

3. Are the descriptive details **interesting**?

Self   1 2 3 4

Partner 1 2 3 4

4. Do **linking words** connect the details?

Self   1 2 3 4

Partner 1 2 3 4

5. Does the ending **sum up** the description and tell the writer's **feelings** about it?

Self   1 2 3 4

Partner 1 2 3 4

▶ Now revise your paragraph to make it stronger.

Grammar USING ADJECTIVES THAT COMPARE

An **adjective** is a word that tells about, or describes, a noun. Adjectives can help compare two or more people, places, or things.

- To use an adjective to **compare two things**, add *-er* to the adjective or use the word *more*.

- To use an adjective to **compare three or more things**, add *-est* to the adjective or use the word *most*.

Example

Adjective Comparing Two Things	Adjective Comparing Three or More Things
Zac is **stronger** than his friend.	He is the **strongest** kid in his class.
Zac is **more athletic** than his friend.	He is the **most athletic** student in his class.

▶ **Circle the correct comparing word in the sentences below.**

1. Your burger is [(greasier) greasiest] than this veggie burger.

2. That was the [grosser grossest] meal I've ever eaten.

3. This salad is the [more most] healthy meal you could eat.

4. Americans eat [larger largest] portions than the Japanese.

5. Meat should be the [smaller smallest] portion on our plate.

6. Pizza is probably [more most] tasty than bugs.

▶ **Rewrite the sentences to compare three or more things correctly.**

7. Zac is the <u>more</u> active person in his family.

_____

8. Zac now runs the <u>faster</u> mile of all his classmates.

_____

9. Who gets the <u>more</u> exercise in your class?

_____

10. Americans should try to be the <u>healthier</u> people in the world.

_____

Edit ➤ *Take a close look at each of the sentences in your draft on page 205. Do they use adjectives that compare correctly? Fix the ones that don't.*

Proofreading USING QUOTATION MARKS

Quotation marks show the exact words of a speaker.

- The first word of a quotation is usually capitalized.
- Punctuation usually goes inside the second quotation.

Example

Correct	Incorrect
Annie asked, "Where is the milk?"	Annie asked, "where is the milk?"
"It's in the fridge," Yvonne said.	"It's in the fridge", Yvonne said.

▶ Find and correct five errors in this paragraph.

Student Model

> The food I most perfer is chocolate ice cream. When I *see* it on a sugar cone, I can't help but say, Yum, yum, yum! It smells so sweet. The sound of a crunchy cone delights my ears. But the taste of rich, dark chocolate is the best. Nothing apeals to me more than the feel of cold ice cream in my mouth. I think ice cream is the better food in the world!

Check and Correct

- ❑ Circle two spelling errors and correct them.
- ❑ Insert two missing quotation marks.
- ❑ Correct one error with a comparison.

Edit *Look at the sentences in your draft on page 205. Are all the quotations formed and punctuated correctly? Fix the ones that aren't.*

Final Draft/Present

▶ **Write a final draft of your paragraph on paper or the computer. Check it again and correct any errors before you present it.**

Coach

Abby Pando is the head coach of a girls' track team. A coach does more than teach the skills of a sport. Coaching is also about motivating athletes. To motivate her team, Abby tells them, "I was a competitor my entire life." They trust her because she knows what she's talking about.

Name: Abby Pando

Hometown: Fort Stockton, Texas

Job: Head Girls' Track Coach

Duties:
• runs practice and workouts
• keeps track of team budget
• motivates and encourages athletes
• provides health and nutrition advice

Skills:
• ability to teach training techniques
• knowledge of sports medicine
• motivational skills

Similar Jobs:
• personal trainer
• physical therapist

Pay: $40,000 per year

Education: Bachelor's Degree and teaching certificate

Abby Pando has her team run time trials at after-school practice.

Ask Yourself

1. **Underline** Mark the level of education needed for this job.

2. **Circle** In the "skills" list, mark the skills you already have.

3. Would you want this job?

☐ Yes   ☐ Maybe   ☐ No

Analyzing a Nutrition Label

Abby makes sure her team stays healthy. Without a healthy diet, runners won't do their best. Food labels help Abby find out what nutrients the food offers. Check out the label below. Then answer the questions.

Nutrition Facts

Serving Size 1 muffin
Servings Per Container 2

Amount Per Serving

Calories 250   Calories from Fat 110

	% Daily Value*
Total Fat 12g	**18%**
Saturated Fat 3g	**15%**
Cholesterol 30mg	**10%**
Sodium 47mg	**20%**
Total Carbohydrate 31g	**10%**
Dietary Fiber 3g	**12%**
Sugars 5g	
Protein 5g	

▶ **Fill in the circle next to the correct answer.**

1. What makes up one serving of muffins?
- Ⓐ one package
- Ⓑ two packages
- Ⓒ two muffins
- Ⓓ one muffin

2. What percentage of your daily value of sodium (salt) does one serving have?
- Ⓐ 18%
- Ⓑ 15%
- Ⓒ 10%
- Ⓓ 20%

3. If you ate two packages of muffins, how much cholesterol would you have eaten?
- Ⓐ 18% of your daily value
- Ⓑ 72% of your daily value
- Ⓒ 12% of your daily value
- Ⓓ 40% of your daily value

4. Fiber is important to your diet. How much does a muffin have?
- Ⓐ 3 grams
- Ⓑ 5 grams
- Ⓒ 12 grams
- Ⓓ 30 mg

5. Would you eat this muffin? Explain.

_____

_____

Comprehension

▶ **Fill in the bubble next to the best answer.**

1. What types of foods do school chefs want to serve to kids?
   Ⓐ cinnamon rolls
   Ⓑ burgers and cookies
   Ⓒ fruits and vegetables
   Ⓓ bugs

Here's a tip!
Read over your answers carefully. Double-check that you filled in the answers in the correct places.

2. How do bugs and burgers compare in terms of health benefits?
   Ⓐ Bugs are healthier because they have less fat than burgers.
   Ⓑ Bugs are healthier because they are crunchier than burgers.
   Ⓒ Burgers are healthier because they come from cows.
   Ⓓ Bugs and burgers have the exact same health benefits.

3. How many people around the world eat bugs?
   Ⓐ Only a few—about 10 percent.
   Ⓑ About half—about 50 percent.
   Ⓒ Most—about 80 percent.
   Ⓓ All people around the world eat bugs.

4. Which of these is NOT a good way to exercise?
   Ⓐ walking to school
   Ⓑ playing sports
   Ⓒ playing video games
   Ⓓ riding a bike

5. What is one way to eat more healthfully?
   Ⓐ Pay attention to the food groups and daily recommended amounts.
   Ⓑ Eat what is most popular with your friends.
   Ⓒ Only eat fresh fruits and vegetables.
   Ⓓ Eat only things that taste good.

Vocabulary

▶ **Fill in the circle next to the correct definitions of the underlined words.**

1. We have to run a mile in under ten minutes to <u>satisfy</u> our coach.
- Ⓐ to please someone by doing enough
- Ⓒ to make someone sleepy
- Ⓑ to make someone angry by doing little
- Ⓓ to make someone sad

2. Books about sports <u>appeal</u> to me more than books about science.
- Ⓐ to be disgusting
- Ⓒ to seem likeable
- Ⓑ to be harder to read
- Ⓓ to be longer

3. My family eats a <u>variety</u> of food, but burritos are our favorite.
- Ⓐ food from Mexico
- Ⓒ colorful
- Ⓑ selection of different things
- Ⓓ large amount

▶ **Choose the word that best fills in the blank.**

4. I think chocolate ice cream is _____ to vanilla.
- Ⓐ prefer
- Ⓒ preferable
- Ⓑ preferring
- Ⓓ preferless

▶ **Choose the synonym for the underlined word.**

5. Vegetables are part of a <u>nutritious</u> diet.
- Ⓐ unhealthy
- Ⓒ exciting
- Ⓑ boring
- Ⓓ healthful

Short Answer

▶ **Use what you've read in this Workshop to answer the question below. Check your spelling and grammar.**

Describe what you ate for breakfast today. Was it healthy? Was it delicious?

_____

_____

_____

Workshop 9
Nonfiction and Literature

Comprehension Focus
Make Inferences

READINGS
1 Ruby Bridges >> Nonfiction Article
2 Through My Eyes >> Autobiography
3 Life Doesn't Frighten Me >> Poetry

No Small Hero

In 1960, Ruby Bridges was a first grader. On the day she started school, Ruby made history. She was the first— and only—African-American student to go to her school.

Ruby became a hero of the civil rights movement. She was brave. She was strong. She was just six years old.

VOCABULARY BUILDER

◎ Target Word ▶ Read the Target Words. Rate each one using the scale below.*	Meaning ▶ Read the Target Word meanings. Write in the missing ones.	Example ▶ Finish the Target Word examples below. Write in the missing ones.
admire *ad•mire* *(verb)* ① ② ③		Some people that I admire are . . .
frightened *fright•ened* *(adjective)* ① ② ③	afraid	
influence *in•flu•ence* *(verb)* ① ② ③		I would like to influence . . .
opportunity *op•por•tu•ni•ty* *(noun)* ① ② ③	a chance to do something	
serious *se•ri•ous* *(adjective)* ① ② ③		An ambulance worker has to be **serious** about her job.

*Rating Scale
① = I don't know it at all.
② = I've seen it before.
③ = I know it and use it.

🔅 The Big Idea

Write ▶ What is this article mainly about?

_____

_____

_____

VOCABULARY BUILDER

◎ Target Word

ignore
ig•nore (verb)

Rate it: ①   ②   ③

Meaning

_____

_____

Example

_____

_____

_____

React

If you were Ruby, would you have wanted to go to William Frantz Public School? Why or why not?

Ruby Bridges

One little girl fought for equal rights

Ruby Bridges became a hero at the age of six. In 1954, the United States Supreme Court had made a decision. They ruled that it was unfair for African-American children and white children to go to separate schools. But for many years after that, states in the South **ignored** the order for schools to integrate.

Louisiana was one of those states. New Orleans, the city where Ruby's family lived, was given a deadline. They had to start integrating schools by September 1960. That was the year that Ruby would be a first grader.

At the end of kindergarten, African-American kindergartners were given a test. Children who passed would be allowed to go to the white schools. The test was hard. But Ruby did well. She was chosen to attend William Frantz Public School. Three other children would attend a different school.

Ruby would get a better education at the new school. But it came at a great cost. Many people were angry. They threatened Ruby. White parents wouldn't let their children be in her class. Her principal treated her unfairly. And her father was fired from his job.

But Ruby proved that one small person can make a big difference. ⏩END

Words to Know!   **integrate**   to include people of all races

Make Inferences

When you **make inferences**, you form ideas about things that are not directly stated in the text. To make inferences:

- Look for a situation in the text in which the author gives clues but doesn't state exactly what is happening.
- Think about what you already know about the situation.
- Combine the text clues with your own experiences or knowledge to make an inference.

▶ **Fill in this chart to make an inference about "Ruby Bridges."**

What I Learned From Reading

White parents wouldn't let their children go to school with Ruby.

What I Already Know

My Inference

Through

💡 The Big Idea

Write ▶ What is this article mainly about?

_____

_____

_____

VOCABULARY BUILDER

◎ Target Word

surround

sur•round (verb)

Rate it: ① ② ③

Meaning

_____

_____

Example

_____

_____

_____

❗ React

What do you learn about Ruby Bridges from looking at her photo?

My Eyes

by Ruby Bridges

When Ruby Bridges grew up, she told her story in a book titled *Through My Eyes*. Parts of the book appear here.

November 14, 1960

My mother took special care getting me ready for school. When somebody knocked on my door that morning, my mother saw four serious-looking white men, dressed in suits and wearing armbands. They were U.S. federal marshals. They had come to drive us to school and stay with us all day. I learned later they were carrying guns.

I remember climbing into the back seat of the marshals' car with my mother, but I don't remember feeling frightened. William Frantz Public School was only five blocks away, so one of the marshals in the front seat told my mother right away what we should do when we got there.

"Let us get out of the car first," the marshal said. "Then you'll get out, and the four of us will **surround** you and your daughter. We'll walk up to the door together. Just walk straight ahead, and don't look back." ➡

Words to Know!	**federal** having to do with the central government of a country

Make Inferences

1. **Underline** ▶ Who came to Ruby's house on her first day of school?

2. **Write** ▶ What do you know about why marshals and police officers protect people?

_____

_____

_____

_____

3. **Write** ▶ What inference can you make about Ruby's safety?

_____

_____

_____

_____

Active Reading

Write What did people in the crowd do when Ruby arrived at school?

_____

_____

_____

Angry protesters stand across the street from Ruby's school.

When we were near the school, my mother said, "Ruby, I want you to behave yourself today and do what the marshals say."

We drove down North Galvez Street to the point where it crosses Alvar. I remember looking out of the car as we pulled up to the Frantz school. There were barricades and people shouting and policemen everywhere. I thought maybe it was Mardi Gras, the carnival that takes place in New Orleans every year. Mardi Gras was always noisy.

As we walked through the crowd, I didn't see any faces. I guess that's because I wasn't very tall and I was surrounded by the marshals. People yelled and threw things. I could see the school building, and it looked bigger and nicer than my old school. When we climbed the high steps to the front door, there were policemen in uniforms at the top. The policemen at the door and the crowd behind us made me think this was an important place.

It must be college, I thought to myself. ➡

 React

Write How would you have felt if you were Ruby?

_____

_____

_____

_____

Words to Know!	**barricades** barriers to stop people from getting past a certain point

🔆 Active Reading

Write ▶ How did Ruby spend her first day of school?

_____

_____

_____

VOCABULARY BUILDER
◎ Target Word

confusion

con•fu•sion (noun)

Rate it: ① ② ③

Meaning

_____

_____

Example

_____

_____

_____

❗ React

What do you think Ruby was thinking about when she sat in the office?

The First Day at William Frantz

Once we were inside the building, the marshals walked us up a flight of stairs. The school office was at the top. My mother and I went in and were told to sit in the principal's office. The marshals sat outside. There were windows in the room where we waited. That meant everybody passing by could see us. I remember noticing everyone was white.

All day long, white parents rushed into the office. They were upset. They were arguing and pointing at us. When they took their children to school that morning, the parents hadn't been sure whether William Frantz would be integrated that day or not. After my mother and I arrived, they ran into classrooms and dragged their children out of the school. From behind the windows in the office, all I saw was **confusion**. I told myself that this must be the way it is in a big school.

That whole first day, my mother and I just sat and waited. We didn't talk to anybody. I remember watching a big, round clock on the wall. When it was 3:00 and time to go home, I was glad. I had thought my new school would be hard, but the first day was easy.

Ruby and her mother leave William Frantz after the first day of school.

My First White Teacher

On the second day, my mother and I drove to school with the marshals. The crowd outside the building was ready. Racists spat at us and shouted things. . . .

I tried not to pay attention. When we finally got into the building, my new teacher was there to meet us. Her name was Mrs. Henry. She was young and white. ➡

Words to Know!	**racists** people who believe that some races of people are better than others

Make Inferences

1. **Underline** Find a detail that shows that Ruby had an unusual first day of school.

2. **Write** How is Ruby different from other students at William Frantz?

_____

_____

_____

_____

3. **Write** Why was Ruby's first day of school so unusual?

_____

_____

_____

_____

_____

Active Reading

Star What was strange about Ruby's classroom?

VOCABULARY BUILDER

⊙ **Target Word**

imitate
im•i•tate (verb)

Rate it: ① ② ③

Meaning

_____

_____

Example

_____

_____

_____

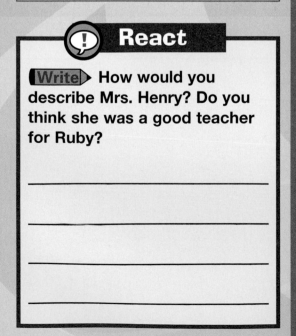 **React**

Write How would you describe Mrs. Henry? Do you think she was a good teacher for Ruby?

_____

_____

_____

_____

I had not spent time with a white person before, so I was uneasy at first. Mrs. Henry led us upstairs to the second floor. As we went up, we hardly saw anyone else in the building. The white students were not coming to class. The halls were so quiet, I could hear the noise the marshals' shoes made on the shiny hardwood floors.

Mrs. Henry took us into a classroom and said to have a seat. When I looked around, the room was empty. There were rows of desks, but no children. I thought we were too early, but Mrs. Henry said we were right on time. My mother sat down at the back of the room. I took a seat up front, and Mrs. Henry began to teach.

Through the Winter With Mrs. Henry

After Christmas, my teacher and I settled into a routine. It was odd to be the only child in class, but I finally decided this was the way it was going to be here at the Frantz school. Being Mrs. Henry's only student wasn't a chore. It was fun and felt sort of special. She was more like my best friend than just an ordinary teacher. She was a loving person, and I knew she cared about me.

Mrs. Henry and I always had fun. We did everything together, reading and word puzzles, spelling and math. We sang songs and played games. Since I couldn't go outside, we pushed desks out of the way and did jumping jack exercises.

I know now that Mrs. Henry influenced me a great deal that year. She had a polite, kind manner

Words to Know! **routine** a regular way of doing things

Ruby Bridges finished first grade at William Frantz Public School.

 Fact and Opinion

1. **Underline** A fact is a statement that can be proven. Find one fact about Ruby's classroom.

2. **Circle** An opinion tells what someone thinks. It may seem correct, but it cannot be proven. Find one of Ruby's opinions about Mrs. Henry.

Review:
Compare and Contrast

1. **Write** How did the people outside the school treat Ruby?

_____

_____

_____

2. **Write** How did Mrs. Henry treat Ruby?

_____

_____

_____

that I admired. In fact, I began to **imitate** her. Little by little, I grew to love Mrs. Henry. We became very attached to each other.

The End of First Grade

Near the end of the year, Mrs. Henry and I finally had company. A few white children began coming back to school, and I got an opportunity to visit with them once or twice. Even though these children were white, I still knew nothing about racism or integration. I had picked up bits and pieces over the months from being around adults and hearing them talk, but nothing was clear to me. The light dawned one day when a little white boy refused to play with me. ➡

Active Reading

Star How does Ruby's school year end?

VOCABULARY BUILDER

Target Word

quarrel

quar•rel (verb)

Rate it: ③

Meaning

_____

_____

Example

_____

_____

_____

React

If you were Ruby Bridges would you want to go back to the same school for second grade? Why or why not?

At that moment, it all made sense to me. I finally realized that everything had happened because I was black. I remember feeling a little stunned. It was all about the color of my skin. I wasn't angry at the boy, because I understood. His mother had told him not to play with me, and he was obeying her. I would have done the same thing. If my mama said not to do something, I didn't do it.

The next thing I knew, it was June. That incredible year was over. Oddly enough, it ended quietly. I don't remember any special good-byes as I headed off for summer vacation. I was sorry to leave Mrs. Henry, but I somehow thought she would be my teacher again in the fall and forever.

Words to Know!	**realized** understood

TEXT FEATURE Reading a Time Line

Key Events in Civil Rights History

1947

Jackie Robinson
Jackie Robinson starts playing for the Brooklyn Dodgers baseball team. This leads to the end of segregation in the sport.

1954

Brown vs. Board of Education
The Supreme Court rules that school segregation is unfair. Schools must integrate.

1960

Ruby Bridges
Ruby Bridges integrates her elementary school in New Orleans, Louisiana.

Mrs. Henry gave me excellent grades at the end of the year, but I was told that the school principal threatened to change them. She said I had received so much individual attention that the grades weren't accurate. Mrs. Henry was angry and **quarreled** with the principal. Mrs. Henry was sad for me and very upset that the principal could be so mean to me. I don't know to this day whether the grades were changed or not. But it didn't matter. The principal couldn't change what was in my head. END

Skills Check

1. **Underline** Find a detail that tells what the principal did at the end of the year.

2. **Write** Why do you think some people treat others unfairly?

_____

_____

_____

_____

3. **Write** What can you infer about the way the principal felt about Ruby?

_____

_____

_____

A time line shows key events in the order they happened.

1964

Civil Rights Act

President Lyndon B. Johnson signs the Civil Rights Act of 1964. This ends segregation in all public places.

1. What does this time line show?

Ⓐ President Lyndon B. Johnson's life
Ⓑ *Brown vs. Board of Education*
Ⓒ key events in civil rights history
Ⓓ the life of Ruby Bridges

2. When did Jackie Robinson join the Brooklyn Dodgers?

Ⓐ 1947
Ⓑ 1954
Ⓒ 1960
Ⓓ 1964

3. Who signed the Civil Rights Act?

Ⓐ Jackie Robinson
Ⓑ President Lyndon B. Johnson
Ⓒ Ruby Bridges
Ⓓ the Supreme Court

Active Reading

Write> List three things that don't frighten the speaker of the poem.

1._____

_____

2._____

_____

3._____

_____

Life Doesn't Frighten Me

by Maya Angelou

Shadows on the wall
Noises down the hall
Life doesn't frighten me at all
Bad dogs barking loud
Big ghosts in a cloud
Life doesn't frighten me at all.

Mean old Mother Goose
Lions on the loose
They don't frighten me at all
Dragons breathing flame
On my counterpane
That doesn't frighten me at all.

React

Write> Do you feel the same way the poet does about being afraid? Why or why not?

_____

_____

_____

_____

I go boo
Make them shoo
I make fun
Way they run
I won't cry
So they fly
I just smile
They go wild
Life doesn't frighten me at all.

Tough guys in a fight
All alone at night
Life doesn't frighten me at all.

Panthers in the park
Strangers in the dark
No, they don't frighten me at all.

That new classroom where
Boys all pull my hair
(Kissy little girls
With their hair in curls)
They don't frighten me at all.

Don't show me frogs and snakes
And listen for my scream,
If I'm afraid at all
It's only in my dreams.

I've got a magic charm
That I keep up my sleeve,
I can walk the ocean floor
And never have to breathe.

Life doesn't frighten me at all
Not at all
Not at all.
Life doesn't frighten me at all. (END)

📖 **Literary Elements:**
Rhyme and Repetition

Rhyme is two or more words that have ending syllables with the same sound.

1. **Circle** ▸ Find the words that rhyme in the poem.

Repetition is words, phrases, or sentences that are used over and over again.

2. **Underline** ▸ Find the phrases that repeat in the poem.

📖 **Cross-Text Analysis**

1. **Write** ▸ How does this poem remind you of Ruby Bridges?

_____

_____

_____

_____

_____

_____

Take the WORD CHALLENGE

START

1 Pick one. Read the activities below. Which would you most like the opportunity to do?

- [ ] visit the moon
- [ ] star in a movie
- [ ] climb a mountain
- [ ] dive off a high board

2 Evaluate. Write *A* next to the people you admire. Write *DA* next to the people you don't admire.

_____ a thief

_____ a nurse at the hospital

_____ a parent

_____ a famous singer

3 Noun Endings

To show more than one person, place, or thing, add an *-s* to most nouns.

- If a noun ends in *ss, s, x, ch,* or *sh,* add *-es* to make it plural, as in *buses* and *dresses.*

- If a noun ends in a consonant and *y,* change the *y* to *i* and add *-es* to make it plural, as in *spies.*

- Plus, watch out for irregular plurals like *mice,* the plural of *mouse.* These don't follow the rules!

Being a clown gives you lots of **opportunities.**

Will I have the **opportunity** to get a pie in my face?

Write the plural form of each word below.

Singular	Plural		Singular	Plural
teacher	_____		box	_____
dress	_____		goose	_____
bench	_____		penny	_____

4 Fill in. Complete the sentences with imitate and surrounded.

Last night, I had a really weird dream. At first, I thought I was

_____ by birds. The I realized I was hearing

a bunch of cats who knew how to _____ bird

sounds. Freaky!

5 Check them. Check off the times you would need to be serious.

- [ ] while taking a test
- [ ] at a birthday party
- [ ] in gym class
- [ ] at the doctor's office

6
Decide. Put an *H* next to things that are hard to ignore. Put an *E* next to things that are easy to ignore.

_____ water dripping on your head while you're in bed

_____ neighbors having a **quarrel** on your block

_____ homework that is due tomorrow

_____ your friends teasing you

7
Think about it. Match each person or animal on the left to the creature on the right that it is most frightened by.

mouse	**spider**
child	**monster**
fly	**cat**

8
Using a Dictionary

Guide words are the words on the top of dictionary pages. They tell the first and last words listed on those pages.

Write these Target Words next to the words that could be their guide words:

admire	frightened	quarrel

Guide Words	**Target Word**
quantity, quartz	_____
achieve, average	_____
familiar, fuel	_____

9
Evaluate. Who has the most influence on your life? Check two.

☐ the President of the United States

☐ your principal

☐ the local weather person

☐ a police officer

☐ your classmates

10
Check them. Which of these situations would cause *you* a lot of confusion?

☐ a sudden, huge rainstorm

☐ new hours at the library

☐ new road signs all over town

☐ a blackout

FINISH

Writing Focus
Personal Narrative

A **personal narrative** tells about an event in the writer's life.

▶ **Read José's personal narrative about a time when he had to be brave.**

Student Model

The Phone Call

by José Vargas

One day, my mom started having an asthma attack after we came home from the park. The first thing I did was ask her if she was okay. She looked serious as she pointed to the phone. Then, I called 911. I was frightened, but I knew what I had to do. In a shaky voice, I explained what was wrong. After that, paramedics came and helped my mom breathe. We rode to the hospital in the ambulance. When it was over, people said they admired my bravery. I'm just glad my mom had taught me what to do. It saved her life.

Parts of a Personal Narrative

▶ **Find these parts of José's personal narrative.**

1. Underline the sentence that tells about the **event**.
2. Check three important **details** that tell about the event.
3. Number these details in the **time order** they happened.
4. Circle the **linking words** that connect the details.
5. Put a star before the sentences that **sum up** the event and tell the writer's **feelings** about it.

Brainstorm

▶ Read the writing prompt in the middle of the idea web. Then use the boxes to help you brainstorm your ideas.

At School

On the Playground

Writing Prompt:
Tell about a time when you had to be brave.

At the Doctor's Office

Someplace Else

Plan Your Paragraph

Writing Prompt: Tell about a time when you had to be brave.

▶ Use this chart to plan and organize your paragraph.

Word Choices

_____

_____

_____

_____

_____

Event

• One day, . . .

• Once, . . .

• When I was . . .

Detail 1

• The first thing . . .

• At first, . . .

• First, I . . .

Detail 2

• Then, . . .

• Next, . . .

• The second thing . . .

Detail 3

• After that, . . .

• Finally, . . .

• Later, . . .

Ending

• When it was over, . . .

• In the end, . . .

• Looking back now, . . .

Write Your Paragraph

▶ Use this writing frame to write a first draft of your paragraph.

_____
(title)

One day, _____

_____

_____

The first thing _____

_____

_____

Then, _____

_____

_____

After that, _____

_____

_____

When it was over, _____

_____

_____

_____

Revise

▶ Rate your paragraph. Then have a writing partner rate it.

Scoring Guide			
weak	okay	good	strong
1	2	3	4

1. Does the beginning clearly state the **event**?

Self	1	2	3	4
Partner	1	2	3	4

2. Are there **details** that tell about the event?

Self	1	2	3	4
Partner	1	2	3	4

3. Are the details arranged in the **time order** they happened?

Self	1	2	3	4
Partner	1	2	3	4

4. Do **linking words** connect the details?

Self	1	2	3	4
Partner	1	2	3	4

5. Does the ending **sum up** the event and tell the writer's **feelings** about it?

Self	1	2	3	4
Partner	1	2	3	4

▶ Now revise your paragraph to make it stronger.

Grammar USING ADVERBS

An **adjective** describes a person, place, or thing. An **adverb** describes a verb, adjective, or another adverb. Many adverbs end in *-ly*.

• Use adverbs to make your writing more precise.

Example

Adjective	Adverb
Ruby went to a **different** school.	She was treated **differently** from whites.
There were **unfair** laws in many states.	Many people were treated **unfairly**.
Some **brave** people demanded justice.	They **bravely** stood up for their beliefs.

▶ **Circle the correct form of the word in brackets in the sentences below. Write whether you've circled an adjective or an adverb.**

1. Ruby waited [patient (patiently)] in the office. ___adverb___

2. People were [angry angrily] when Ruby arrived at school. _____

3. Her first day at school passed [slowly slow]. _____

4. Ruby learned [quick quickly] at her new school. _____

5. Mrs. Henry was very [politely polite] to Ruby. _____

6. Other students [final finally] returned to school. _____

▶ **Rewrite the sentences using the correct form of the adverb.**

7. The laws changed <u>slow</u> in some states.

_____

8. Ruby's family took education <u>serious</u>.

_____

9. Students should all be treated <u>equal</u>.

_____

10. Some whites responded <u>violent</u> to integration.

_____

Edit ▶ *Take a close look at each of the sentences in your draft on page 233. Do they use adverbs correctly? If not, fix them.*

Usage CORRECTING SENTENCE FRAGMENTS

Each **sentence** must state a complete idea.

- You can often add a subject or a verb to a sentence fragment to form a complete sentence.

Example

Correct	Incorrect
Mrs. Henry was a kind teacher.	Was a kind teacher.
Ruby got excellent grades.	Ruby excellent grades.

▶ **Find and correct five errors in this paragraph.**

Student Model

Last June, I learned how to swim. First, Mom enrolled me in the classes. Then, she told me about them. I had always been fritened of water, but I couldn't argue with her. The next Saturday, she drove me to the pool. The teacher knew I was scared. He gave me floats for my arms to help me adjust. Next, taught me to kick. Soon, I was swimming. Like a fish. It was definite the most serius challenge I ever faced!

Check and Correct

- ❏ Circle two spelling errors and correct them.
- ❏ Underline one incorrectly formed adverb and correct it.
- ❏ Correct two sentence fragments.

Edit *Look at the sentences in your draft on page 233. Do they all contain a subject and a verb? If not, fix them.*

Final Draft/Present

▶ **Write a final draft of your paragraph on paper or the computer. Check it again and correct any errors before you present it.**

Ruby Bridges

Ruby Bridges was born in Mississippi in 1954. A few years later, her parents moved to New Orleans in search of better jobs. There, Ruby found herself in the middle of the civil rights movement. She became one of four first graders to integrate the city's white schools.

Ruby went on to graduate from an integrated high school. She became a travel agent, got married, and raised four sons. Later in life, Ruby decided to use her experiences at William Frantz Public School to help inspire people.

Ruby went back to her old elementary school to do volunteer work. Soon, she started the Ruby Bridges Foundation, which works to end racism. Today, she travels the country talking to students and adults about her experiences. Sometimes she and Mrs. Henry visit schools together.

As a child, Ruby took small steps toward the front door of her school. Today she continues to take steps toward equality for all Americans.

Ruby Bridges signs her book for students at a school in Connecticut.

BOOKS:

Through My Eyes

"I sometimes feel I lost something that year. I feel as if I lost my childhood."

Ask Yourself

1. **Underline** ▶ Find where Ruby Bridges was born.

2. **Circle** ▶ Find what the Ruby Bridges Foundation does.

3. Would you like to read the rest of Ruby Bridges' book? Explain.

_____

_____

_____

Make Inferences

▶ **Fill in this chart to make inferences about "November 14, 1960."**

What I Learned From Reading

Ruby thought the crowd might be
celebrating Mardi Gras.
_____
_____

What I Already Know

_____
_____
_____
_____
_____

My Inference

_____
_____
_____
_____

Reading a News Web Site

Ruby Bridges is still making headlines today. Where can you find the latest information on her? Check out a news Web site like the one below.

▶ **Fill in the circle next to each correct answer.**

1. What is the name of this Web site?

Ⓐ Special Reports
Ⓑ Ruby Bridges Today
Ⓒ Scholastic News
Ⓓ Games & Quizzes

2. What are you most likely to see if you click "Read the Full Story"?

Ⓐ a movie review
Ⓑ an article about Ruby Bridges
Ⓒ a game
Ⓓ a list of special reports

3. How many links does this page have for movies?

Ⓐ two
Ⓑ one
Ⓒ none
Ⓓ four

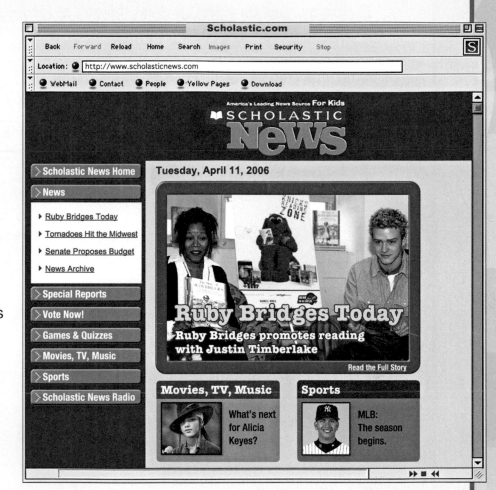

4. What do you think will happen if you click "Scholastic News Radio"?

Ⓐ You'll see a picture of a radio.
Ⓑ You'll get an article about radios.
Ⓒ You'll hear someone reading the news.
Ⓓ You'll get to play a game.

5. Which button would you click to get scores for recent baseball games?

Ⓐ Games & Quizzes
Ⓑ Vote Now!
Ⓒ Scholastic News Radio
Ⓓ Sports

Comprehension

▶ **Fill in the circle next to the correct answer.**

1. Why was Ruby Bridges chosen to go to William Frantz Public School?

Ⓐ She was chosen because she was so brave.

Ⓑ Ruby lived very close to that school.

Ⓒ She did well on a test given at the end of kindergarten.

Ⓓ Her best friends went there.

2. What was Ruby's main problem in first grade?

Ⓐ She got into a fight with her best friend.

Ⓑ She was the only African-American student in an all-white school.

Ⓒ Her parents wanted to move.

Ⓓ She had a mean teacher.

> **Here's a Tip.**
> Check your work against the reading you're being tested on. Make sure your answer agrees with what's in the reading.

3. Which words best describe Mrs. Henry, Ruby's first-grade teacher?

Ⓐ kind and loving

Ⓑ lazy and careless

Ⓒ mean and unfair

Ⓓ angry and grumpy

4. The poet Maya Angelou probably wrote "Life Doesn't Frighten Me" to _____.

Ⓐ make people have bad dreams

Ⓑ remember what Ruby Bridges did

Ⓒ make fun of people's fears

Ⓓ help people feel brave

5. How are Ruby Bridges and the speaker of the poem similar?

Ⓐ They both make new friends.

Ⓑ They are both brave in the face of fear.

Ⓒ They are both heroes of the civil rights movement.

Ⓓ They both like their teacher.

Vocabulary

▶ **Fill in the circle next to the correct definition of the underlined word.**

1. The crowds outside the school made Ruby feel <u>frightened</u>.

Ⓐ excited   Ⓒ sad

Ⓑ afraid   Ⓓ lonely

2. Ruby's story can <u>influence</u> people to stand up for what is right.

Ⓐ treat unfairly   Ⓒ frustrate

Ⓑ make happy   Ⓓ have an effect on

3. He had a <u>serious</u> look on his face while taking the test.

Ⓐ thoughtful and solemn   Ⓒ past

Ⓑ low and dangerous   Ⓓ pretend

▶ **Choose the correct plural ending for the underlined word.**

4. Ruby's parents knew that a better school would give Ruby more <u>opportunity</u>.

Ⓐ opportunitism   Ⓒ opportunities

Ⓑ opportunitys   Ⓓ correct as is

▶ **Which are the most likely dictionary guide words for the underlined word?**

5. Many people <u>admire</u> Ruby Bridges for her bravery.

Ⓐ *about* and *zipper*   Ⓒ *goat* and *sing*

Ⓑ *addition* and *average*   Ⓓ *expect* and *courage*

Short Answer

▶ **Use what you've read in this Workshop to answer the question below. Check your spelling and grammar.**

How was Ruby Bridges a hero of the civil rights movement?

_____

_____

_____

Glossary

A glossary is a useful tool found at the back of many books. It contains information about key words in the text. Look at the sample glossary entry below.

The **pronunciation** comes after the entry word. Letters and letter combinations stand for different sounds. The accented syllable is marked in boldfaced letters.

This is an **entry word**—the word you look up. It is divided into syllables.

Look here to find the **meaning** of the entry word.

This tells you what **part of speech** the entry word is.

pa•tient (**pay**-shuhnt)

1. *adjective* Able to wait calmly for a long time. *Tyrone was patient even though his mother was taking a long time.*

2. *noun* Someone receiving treatment from a doctor. *Dr. Ruiz's patient recovered quickly from surgery.*

A **number** appears at the beginning of each meaning when more than one meaning is given for the entry word.

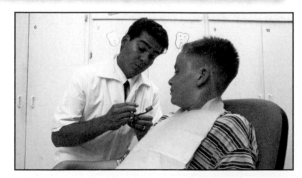

patient

a·ban·don
(uh-**ban**-duhn) *verb*
To leave something you are responsible for. *The pirates had to abandon their ship when it sank.*

ab·sorb
(ab-**zorb**) *verb*
To soak up liquid. *Use a sponge to absorb the extra water.*

a·buse
(uh-**byooss**) *noun*
Harmful treatment of someone. *No one deserves physical or verbal abuse.*

ac·cu·rate
(**ak**-yuh-ruht) *adjective*
Exactly correct. *The cashier gave me accurate change.*

a·chieve
(uh-**cheev**) *verb*
To succeed in doing something. *Carla works hard to achieve top grades in school.*

achieve

ad·just
(uh-**juhst**) *verb*
To move or change something slightly. *I adjusted the painting because it was crooked.*

ad·mire
(ad-**mire**) *verb*
1. To like and respect someone. *I admire my teacher and want to do well in her class.*
2. To look at something and enjoy it. *Luis admired the painting and decided to buy it.*

Suffixes

Admiration ends with the suffix *-tion*. A **suffix** is a letter or group of letters added to the end of a word. The suffix *-tion* changes *admire* from a verb to a noun.

af·fect
(uh-**fekt**) *verb*
To influence or change. *My friends affect my attitude toward school.*

ap·peal
(uh-**peel**) *verb*
1. To seem likable or interesting. *Bright colors appeal to little kids.*
2. To ask for something urgently. *I appealed to the doctor for help.*
3. To ask for a decision by a court of law to be changed. *The defense lawyer plans to appeal the jury's verdict of guilty.*

ap·proach
(uh-**prohch**) *verb*
To move nearer. *A big storm might approach our town by noon.*

as·sist·ance
(uh-**siss**-tuhnss) *noun*
Help. *The door was stuck, so I needed assistance to open it.*

at·ten·tion
(uh-**ten**-shuhn) *noun*
1. The act of paying special care to something or someone. *I gave my dog lots of attention after he was hurt in an accident.*
2. Concentration and careful thought. *Sharla paid attention to the directions and did the project correctly.*

a·vail·a·ble
(uh-**vay**-luh-buhl) *adjective*
1. Possible to get. *The new games will be available in stores next week.*
2. Not busy. *I'm always available to baby-sit on weekends.*

av·er·age
(**av**-uh-rij)
1. *adjective* Usual, or ordinary. *My brother is of average height.*
2. *noun* Based on a calculation that shows what usually happens. *On average, women live longer than men.*
3. *noun* The number calculated by adding a group of figures together and then dividing the sum by the number of figures. *The average of 2, 5, and 14 is 7.*

bar·ri·cade
(**ba**-ruh-*kade*) *noun*
A barrier to stop people from getting past a certain point. *The workers put up a barricade to stop people from entering the construction sight.*

cap·ture
(**kap**-chur) *verb*
To take a person, animal, or place by force. *The police hope to capture the thief soon.*

cen·tu·ry
(**sen**-chuh-ree) *noun*
A period of one hundred years. *The castle was built many centuries ago.*

chal·lenge
(**chal**-uhnj) *noun*
Something difficult to do. *Ashley loves the challenge of a new task.*

com·mo·tion
(kuh-**moh**-shuhn) *noun*
Noisy, excited activity. *The movie star caused a lot of commotion when he walked into the restaurant.*

com·plex
1. (kuhm-**pleks**) *adjective*
With many parts. *The puzzle was very complex.*
2. (**kom**-pleks) *noun*
A group of buildings that are close together and used for the same purpose. *Our apartment is in the building at the back of the complex.*

Multiple-Meaning Words

Complex means "with many parts." It also means "a group of buildings." **Multiple-meaning words** are words that have more than one meaning.

con·cerned
(kuhn-**surnd**) *adjective*
Worried and anxious. *André was concerned that we wouldn't finish our project in time.*

con·di·tion
(kuhn-**dish**-uhn) *noun*
The general state of a person, animal, or thing. *The house was in terrible condition.*

con·fu·sion
(kuhn-**fyoo**-shuhn) *noun*
The state of not understanding something. *Zach caused a lot of confusion when he erased the instructions from the board.*

con·sid·er·ate
(kuhn-**sid**-uh-rit) *adjective*
Thoughtful. *It was considerate of my sister to turn down her music when I went to sleep.*

considerate

con·struct
(kuhn-**struhkt**) *verb*
To build. *The city plans to construct a new highway by the end of the year.*

con·vince
(kuhn-**vinss**) *verb*
To make someone believe or do something. *Jack convinced me that he hadn't stolen the book.*

cul·ture
(**kuhl**-chur) *noun*
The art, ideas, and beliefs of a group of people. *This year, we're studying the culture of Ancient Greece.*

de·fens·i·ble
(di-**fenss**-uh-buhl) *adjective*
Able to defend. *The army made the fort defensible against the enemy.*

de·gree
(di-**gree**) *noun*
1. A unit for measuring temperature. *The temperature hasn't dropped a degree all day.*
2. A title given by a college or university. *My mom has a law degree.*

de·lay
(di-**lay**) *verb*
1. To make someone or something late. *The bad weather delayed Miranda's arrival.*
2. To be late. *Don't delay or we'll miss the bus!*

dis·play
(diss-**play**)
1. *verb* To show something. *Please display your projects at the end of class.*
2. *noun* A public show or exhibition. *My trophies were put on display at school.*

display

doubt
(**dout**) *verb*
To not believe something. *I doubt that my sister will remember my birthday.*

en·cour·age
(en-**kur**-ij) *verb*
To praise or offer support. *My friends always encourage me to do my best.*

en·er·gy
(**en**-ur-jee) *noun*
1. The strength to do things without getting tired. *I took a nap so I would have plenty of energy for the party.*
2. Power. *Turn off the lights when you're done so you don't waste energy.*

e·nor·mous
(i-**nor**-muhss) *adjective*
Very large. *José won an enormous stuffed bear at the carnival.*

en·roll
(en-**rohl**) *verb*
To sign up for. *I plan to enroll in dance class this summer.*

es·tab·lish
(ess-**tab**-lish) *verb*
To found or start something. *My dad plans to establish his own business next year.*

ex·am·ine
(eg-**zam**-uhn) *verb*
To investigate or look into something. *The detective wants to examine the evidence.*

ex·haus·tion
(eg-**zawst**-shuhn) *noun*
The state of being extremely tired. *I didn't get any sleep last night, and now I'm suffering from exhaustion.*

ex·hib·it
(eg-**zib**-it) *noun*
Something put in a public place so people can see it. *The museum has a new exhibit on dinosaurs.*

ex·pect
(ek-**spekt**) *verb*
To think something will happen. *I expect to do well on the test.*

ex·pert
(**ek**-spurt) *noun*
Someone with special knowledge or skills. *An expert on school safety spoke at our school today.*

fa·mil·iar
(fuh-**mil**-yur) *adjective*
Known. *Tessa was happy to see some familiar faces at the park.*

Root Words
The word ***familiar*** comes from the Latin root *familia* which means "family." A **root** is a word or word part from another language that is the basis of an English word.

fam·ine
(**fam**-uhn) *noun*
A serious lack of food. *After the rain ruined the crops, the village faced a famine.*

far·ther
(**far**-THur) *adverb*
At a greater distance than something else. *The new video store is farther away than the old one.*

fed·er·al
(**fed**-ur-uhl) *adjective*
Having to do with the central government of a country. *His case was tried in a federal court rather than a state court.*

Idioms
Someone who gets really upset about something can be "making a ***federal*** case out of it." "To make a federal case" is an **idiom**, an expression that means something different from the separate words.

fierce
(fihrss) *adjective*
Wild and violent. *Many animals become fierce if they are trapped.*

fierce

flee
(flee) *verb*
To run away from danger. *The mouse had to flee the kitchen so the cat wouldn't catch it.*

foot·hill
(fut-hil) *noun*
A low hill at the base of a mountain. *The town was in the foothills of Mt. Everest.*

fright·ened
(frite-uhnd) *adjective*
Afraid. *I was so frightened after watching the horror movie that I couldn't go to sleep.*

fu·el
(fyoo-uhl) *noun*
Something that can be burned for heat or energy, such as coal, wood, gasoline, or natural gas. *The car stopped running because it was out of fuel.*

gaze
(gayz) *verb*
To look at something for a long time. *We gazed in wonder as the sun rose.*

gi·gan·tic
(jye-**gan**-tik) *adjective*
Huge. *The gigantic dog scared my little brother.*

globe
(glohb) *noun*
The world; a round object. *Maria wants to travel around the globe.*

grate·ful
(grayt-fuhl) *adjective*
Thankful. *Marcus was grateful to Amber for helping him with his homework.*

hab·it
(hab-it) *noun*
Something you do often, without thinking. *Making my bed every morning has become a habit.*

hab·i·tat
(hab-uh-*tat*) *noun*
The natural environment of a plant or animal. *The rain forest is the monkey's habitat.*

ig·nore
(ig-**nor**) *verb*
To take no notice of something. *Liza ignored their rude comments.*

Verb Endings

The past-tense form of *ignore* is *ignored*. The present-tense form is *ignoring*. **Verb endings** show when an action takes place. To show an action in the past, you often can add -*ed*. If a verb ends with the letter e, it is usually dropped before adding -*ed* or -*ing*.

im·i·tate
(**im**-uh-tate) *verb*
To copy or mimic someone or something. *My sister hates it when I imitate her.*

im·prove
(im-**proov**) *verb*
To make better. *Kayla wants to improve her math skills this year.*

in·ci·dent
(**in**-suh-duhnt) *noun*
Something serious or violent that happens. *The police looked into the incident at the mall.*

in·flu·ence
(**in**-floo-uhnss)
1. *verb* To have an effect on someone or something. *My friends influence my choice of clothing.*
2. *noun* The effect someone or something has on someone or something else. *I hope to be a good influence on my younger sister.*

in·jure
(**in**-jur) *verb*
To hurt yourself or someone else. *I fell down and injured my knee.*

injure

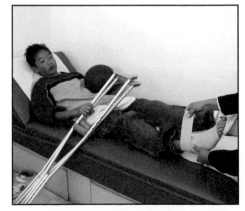

in·sist
(in-**sist**) *verb*
To demand. *My parents insist that I come home right after school.*

in·stinct
(**in**-stingkt) *noun*
1. A natural feeling or behavior that isn't learned or thought out. *Ducks swim by instinct.*
2. Knowing or feeling something without being told about it. *I had an instinct that she was not telling the truth.*

in·te·grate
(**in**-tuh-*grate*) *verb*
1. To include people of all races. *In the 1950s, schools in the South began to integrate.*
2. To combine several things into one whole. *Let's integrate our ideas to tell one story.*

in·ves·ti·gate
(in-**vess**-tuh-gate) *verb*
To look into something. *The detectives said it will take three weeks to investigate the case.*

jour·ney
(**jur**-nee) *noun*
A long trip. *My uncle packed four bags for his journey to China.*

lay·er
(**lay**-ur) *noun*
Something that is placed on or between other things. *I wore a sweater under my coat to add an extra layer of warmth.*

le·gal
(**lee**-guhl) *adjective*
Having to do with the law. *My parents signed many legal papers when they adopted my brother.*

Prefixes

Illegal begins with the prefix *il-*, meaning "not." A **prefix** is a letter or group of letters added to the beginning of a word. A prefix changes the meaning of a word. ***Illegal*** means "not legal to do something."

---

lib·er·ty
(**lib**-ur-tee) *noun*
Freedom. *Many people come to the United States for its liberty.*

lo·cate
(**loh**-kate) *verb*
To find. *Please locate Texas on the map.*

ma·te·ri·al
(mah-**tihr**-ee-uhl) *noun*
Things, such as wood, plastic, and cloth, used to make other things. *The shirt was made of expensive material.*

meth·od
(**meth**-uhd) *noun*
A way of doing something. *Tina had a special method for making her bed.*

mis·sion
(**mish**-uhn) *noun*
1. A church or other place where aid is given to people in need. *Many refugees went to the mission for food and medical care.*
2. A special job or task. *Our mission is to collect clothing for the flood victims.*

ne·ces·si·ty
(nuh-**sess**-uh-tee) *noun*
Something you need to have. *Food and water are basic necessities.*

ne·glect
(ni-**glekt**) *verb*
To fail to take care of something or someone. *Pedro neglected his plants so they died.*

layer

nerve

(**nurv**) *noun*

1. Courage. *You need lots of nerve to be a lion tamer.*
2. Boldness or rudeness. *Justin's got a lot of nerve, answering back like that!*
3. One of many thin fibers that sends messages from your brain to your body. *Alden's dad suffered damage to a nerve in his shoulder in the car accident.*

nerv·ous

(**nur**-vuhss) *adjective*

Worried or frightened about something. *Thunder and lightning make Vince nervous.*

nor·mal·ly

(**nor**-muhl-lee) *adverb*

Usually. *I normally eat cereal for breakfast.*

nu·tri·tious

(noo-**trish**-uhss) *adjective*

Healthy; full of vitamins and minerals. *My parents make a nutritious dinner with lots of vegetables every night.*

ob·vi·ous

(**ob**-vee-uhss) *adjective*

Clear, easy to see. *His frown was an obvious sign that he was unhappy.*

Antonyms

Obvious means "clear and easy to see" and *mysterious* means "not easy to understand." These words are **antonyms**, words that have opposite meanings.

op·po·nent

(uh-**poh**-nuhnt) *noun*

Someone who is against you in a game. *I shook my opponent's hand after the game was over.*

opponent

op·por·tu·ni·ty

(op-ur-**too**-nuh-tee) *noun*

A chance to do something. *Lynda's job gives her the opportunity to travel.*

pa·tient

(**pay**-shuhnt)

1. *adjective* Able to wait calmly for a long time. *Tyrone was patient even though his mother was running late.*
2. *noun* Someone receiving treatment from a doctor. *Dr. Ruiz's patient recovered quickly from surgery.*

per·cent

(pur-**sent**) *noun*

A part of the whole. *Ninety percent of the students voted for Raul when he ran for class president.*

phys·i·cal

(**fiz**-uh-kuhl) *adjective*

Having to do with the body. *In physical education, we learn how to take care of our bodies.*

por·tion

(**por**-shuhn) *noun*

1. An amount of food for one person. *I'd like another portion of mashed potatoes.*
2. A part or piece of something. *He spent a large portion of the evening doing his homework.*

pre·fer

(pri-**fur**) *verb*

To like one thing more than another thing. *Magda prefers oranges to apples.*

pre·serve

(pri-**zurv**)

1. *verb* To keep something from being destroyed. *Let's put the photos in an album to help preserve them.*
2. *noun* Jam or jelly. *Derrick loves toast with apricot preserves.*

pres·sure

(**presh**-ur) *noun*

Strong influence, force, or persuasion. *My dad is under lots of pressure to do well at work.*

pre·vi·ous

(**pree**-vee-uhss) *adjective*

Happening before. *I like this school more than my previous one.*

priv·i·lege

(**priv**-uh-lij) *noun*

A special right or advantage given to a person or groups of people. *The president of the United States enjoys the privilege of living in the White House.*

Noun Endings

To show more than one person, place, or thing, add -*s* to most nouns, like ***privileges***. If a noun ends in *s*, add -*es* to make it plural, like *buses*. If a noun ends in *y*, change the *y* to *i* and add -*es*, like *spies*.

---

pro·ceed

(pruh-**seed**) *verb*

To go ahead with something. *Let's proceed with the meeting even though Alex isn't here yet.*

quar·rel

(**kwor**-uhl) *verb*

To argue or to disagree. *Serena quarreled with her sister over who would get to read the book first.*

quiv·er

(**kwiv**-ur) *verb*

To shake. *Lynda's voice quivered as she gave her oral report.*

rac·ist

(**ray**-sist) *noun*

Someone who believes that some races of people are better than others. *In the 1960s, racists did not want black and white children to go to school together.*

rag·ged·y

(**rag**-eh-dee) *adjective*

Torn and in bad condition. *I wore my favorite skirt so often that it became raggedy.*

range

(**raynj**) *noun*

1. The area where an amimal lives and roams. *We visited a cattle range on our tour of the West.*
2. A line of mountains. *Many of the peaks in the mountain range were covered with snow.*
3. A variety of a group of things. *We could choose from a range of paint colors in art class.*

rap·id·ly

(**rap**-id-lee) *adverb*

Quickly. *He walked rapidly to get to class on time.*

re·al·ize

(**ree**-uh-lize) *verb*

To understand. *Zander realized he was working too hard and needed to take a break.*

re·build

(ree-**bild**) *verb*

To build again. *The city had to rebuild all its offices destroyed by the storm.*

re·gion

(**ree**-juhn) *noun*

An area or section of some place, like a state or country. *In which region of the country do you live?*

re·luc·tant·ly

(ri-**luhk**-tuhnt-lee) *adverb*

Not wanting to do something. *She wanted to talk on the phone, but instead reluctantly did her chores.*

re·ly

(ri-**lye**) *verb*

To need and trust someone. *My mom relies on me to take care of my little brother.*

re·move

(ri-**moov**) *verb*

To take away. *Please remove the empty plates from the table.*

re·un·ion

(ree-**yoon**-yuhn) *noun*

A meeting or gathering. *Our family is having a big reunion this summer.*

roam

(**rohm**) *verb*

To travel aimlessly. *Animals like to roam in the wild.*

roam

route
(**root** or **rout**) *noun*
A way or path to get somewhere. *I walk the same route to school every day.*

rou·tine
(roo-**teen**) *noun*
A regular way or pattern of doing things. *Taking out the garbage is part of my daily routine.*

sa·fa·ri
(suh-**fah**-ree) *noun*
A trip taken to see large animals. *Last year, my cousin got to ride an elephant when he went on a safari.*

safari

sat·is·fy
(**sat**-iss-*fye*) *verb*
To please someone by doing enough or giving enough. *My parents were satisfied with my grades this year.*

scrape
(**skrape**) *verb*
To scratch. *I scraped my knee when I fell off my bike.*

seek
(**seek**) *verb*
To look for. *My teacher is seeking an assistant.*

se·lect
(si-**lekt**) *verb*
To choose. *Please select a movie you'd like to watch.*

se·ri·ous
(**sihr**-ee-uhss) *adjective*
1. Thoughtful and solemn. *After we lost the game, everyone was serious on the bus ride home.*
2. Very bad or dangerous. *She has a serious illness.*

source
(**sorss**) *noun*
Where something comes from. *What's the source of this drinking water?*

Synonyms
A **source** is "where something comes from" and **origin** is "the place where something began." These words are **synonyms**, words that have similar meanings.

strength·en
(**strengkth**-uhn) *verb*
To make stronger. *My sister works out to strengthen her muscles.*

strug·gle
(**struh**-guhl) *noun*
Something that is hard to do. *Learning to play the piano was a struggle for me.*

sur·round
(suh-**round**) *verb*
To be on every side of something. *A fence surrounds the garden.*

sur·vive
(sur-**vive**) *verb*
1. To stay alive through a dangerous event. *José and his family survived the tornado by staying in the basement.*
2. To continue to live or exist. *Humans need food and water to survive.*

sus·pend
(suh-**spend**) *verb*
1. To force to leave school. *Julie was suspended from school for a week.*
2. To stop something for a short time. *Work was suspended for the holidays.*

sym·bol
(**sim**-buhl) *noun*
A sign or object that represents something else. *On many maps, a small, green pine tree is the symbol for a forest.*

Homophones
Symbol means "an object that represents something else" and **cymbal** means "a musical instrument made of brass, shaped like a plate." These are **homophones**, words that sound alike but have different spellings and meanings.

sys·tem
(**siss**-tuhm) *noun*
A way of doing things. *I need a better system for studying.*

task
(**task**) *noun*
A job. *After the party, I got the annoying task of picking up all the trash.*

ter·ri·fied
(**ter**-uh-fyed) *adjective*
Really scared. *I'm terrified of dogs.*

threat
(**thret**) *noun*
A danger. *A bully is a threat to every student.*

threat

tomb
(**toom**) *noun*
A buriel chamber. *I saw a mummy's tomb at the museum.*

trans·late
(**transs**-late) *verb*
To change speech or writing from one language to another. *Veronica translated the story from English into Spanish.*

trans·port
(**transs**-**port**) *verb*
To move something. *The truck transported chickens.*

trench
(**trench**) *noun*
A long, narrow ditch. *The soldiers stayed in the trenches while the enemy fired at them.*

u·nite
(yoo-**nite**) *verb*
1. To bring together to make a whole. *The states united to form a nation.*
2. To join together to achieve something. *Let's unite to fight poverty.*

val·ue
(**val**-yoo)
1. *noun* What something is worth. *What is the value of this gold watch?*
2. *verb* To think that something is important. *I value Anna's friendship greatly.*

va·ri·e·ty
(vuh-**rye**-uh-tee) *noun*
A selection of different things. *I like a variety of music, including rap and pop.*

voyage

voy·age
(**voi**-ij) *noun*
A long trip, especially in a ship or spacecraft. *My aunt packed six suitcases for her voyage across the Atlantic Ocean.*

worth
(**wurth**) *adjective*
Deserving, or good enough for. *It was worth spending time on the project because I got a good grade.*

Compound Words
Worthwhile is a compound word. A **compound word** is made up of two smaller words, like *worth+while*.

How to Use the Reading Handbook

This handbook includes the comprehension skills that you mastered in the **rBook**. You can use these directions and charts to review what you know. You can also use them in your other classes, like social studies and science. They can help you understand a new article or story.

Main Idea and Details

The **main idea** is the most important point about a topic. **Details** are the facts that support the main idea. To find the main idea and details:

- Decide what the topic is. Find the main idea about the topic.
- Look for the details that support the main idea.

▶ **Use this chart to identify a main idea and supporting details.**

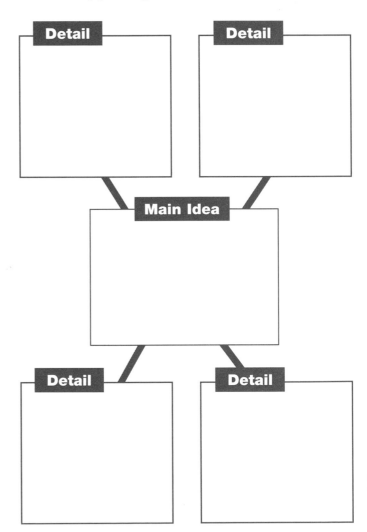

Sequence of Events

Sequence is the order in which events happen. To find a sequence of events:

- Try to remember the order in which events take place.

- Look for times, dates, and signal words, such as *first, then, next, after,* and *finally*.

- When you know the order, check it again. Make sure it makes sense.

▶ **Use this chart to identify a sequence of events.**

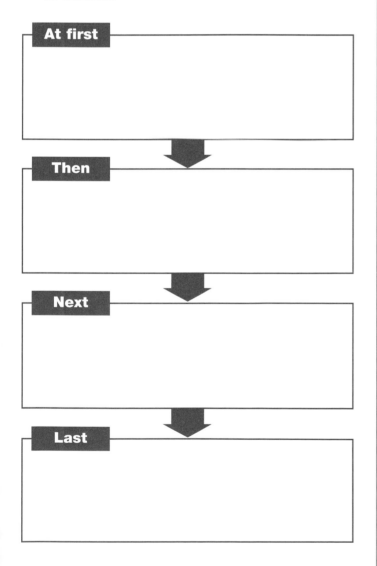

Summarize

A **summary** is a short statement of the most important ideas in a reading. To summarize:

- Find the topic of the reading.

- Look for the most important details about the topic.

- Restate the topic and important details in a short summary. Use your own words.

▶ **Use this chart to identify the topic and important details in a summary.**

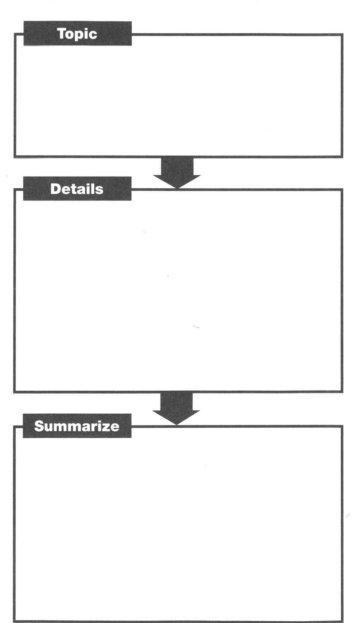

Problem and Solution

A **problem** is a situation or event that causes trouble. A **solution** is what fixes the problem. To find a problem and its solution:

- Look for the problem.
- Find the solution.

▶ **Use this chart to identify a problem and a solution.**

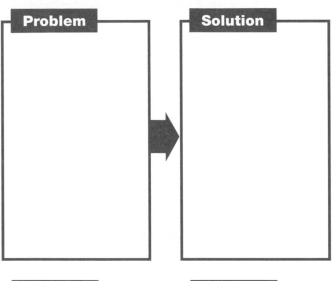

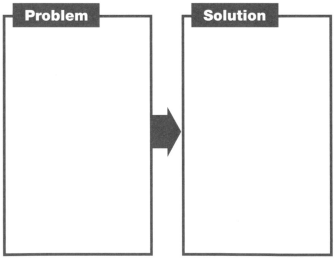

Cause and Effect

A **cause** is the reason something happens. An **effect** is the result of a cause. To find the cause and effect:

- Ask yourself "Why did it happen?" to find the cause.
- Ask yourself "What happened?" to find the effect.
- Look for signal words or phrases such as *because, so, as a result, therefore,* and *for this reason.*

▶ **Use this chart to identify cause-and-effect relationships.**

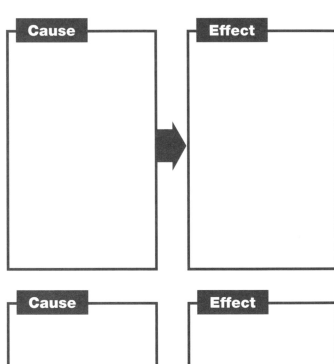

Compare and Contrast

When you **compare**, you tell how two things are the same. When you **contrast**, you tell how they are different. To compare and contrast:

- Ask yourself how two things are the same. Look for signal words such as *both, too, also,* and *in addition.*

- Ask yourself how two things are different. Look for signal words such as *but, rather than, however, unlike,* and *instead.*

▶ Fill in this chart to compare and contrast two things in a reading.

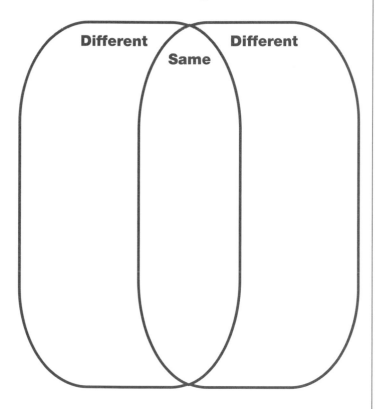

Make Inferences

When you **make inferences**, you form ideas about things that are not directly stated in the text. To make inferences:

- Look for a situation in the text in which the author gives clues but doesn't state exactly what is happening.

- Think about what you already know about the situation.

- Combine the text clues with your own experiences or knowledge to make an inference.

▶ Fill in this chart to make an inference.

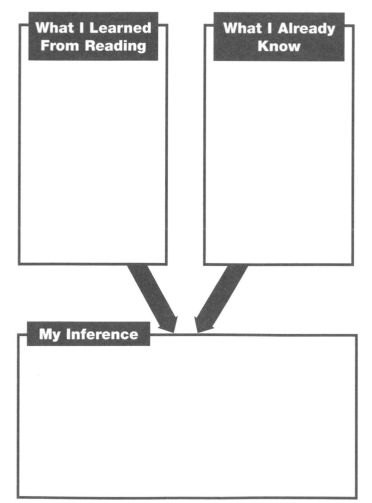

Story Elements

A short story is a brief work of fiction. It focuses on one or two main characters and on a single problem or conflict. To understand a short story, look for four elements:

Setting

Setting refers to the place and time of a story. To analyze the setting:

- Look at the illustrations.

- Look for details that tell *where*. Ask yourself, "What words in the story help me imagine what the place looks like?"

- Look for story details that tell *when*. Ask yourself, "When does this story take place? Is it long ago, in the future, or the present?"

- Pay attention to any changes in the setting and how they affect the story.

Character

A **character** is a person or animal in a story. It's who the story is about. Often stories have several characters. We can identify the main characters because they are the ones the story is mostly about. Characters have special qualities, or traits, that make up their personalities. To analyze a character:

- Look for words the author uses to describe the character, especially adjectives.

- Pay attention to what the character thinks, says, and does.

- Be aware of what other characters say about the character.

- Think about what you already know about people and their behavior.

Plot

Plot refers to what happens in a story, including the problem, the events that lead to solving the problem, and the solution. To analyze the plot:

- Find out what the character's problem is.

- Look at how the character tries to solve the problem.

- Pay attention to what happens to help solve the problem. Look at what happens that gets in the way of solving the problem.

- Think about how the story turns out. Does the character solve the problem? How?

Theme

The **theme** is the message that the author wants you to take away from the story. It often helps you understand the author's purpose, thoughts, and feelings. To analyze theme:

- Think about what the characters do and say.

- Think about what happens to the characters.

- Ask yourself: What does the author want you to know about?

► **Use this chart to keep track of the setting, character, plot, and theme of a story you are reading.**

Story Title: _____

	Part 1	**Part 2**	**Part 3**
Setting	Time: _____ _____ Place: _____ _____ _____	Time: _____ _____ Place: _____ _____ _____	Time: _____ _____ Place: _____ _____ _____
Character	Who is the main character? _____ Describe him/her: _____ _____ _____ _____	How does the character change? _____ _____ _____ _____ _____	What is the character like now? _____ _____ _____ _____ _____
Plot Events	What happens at the beginning of the story? _____ _____ _____ _____ _____	What happens in the middle of the story? _____ _____ _____ _____ _____	How does the story end? _____ _____ _____ _____ _____
Theme	Author's message:		

Literary Terms

author a person who writes a short story, play, poem, novel, article, essay, or book

characters the people in a story. The main character is the most important character.

concrete poetry poetry that has a shape that matches the meaning of the poem or a word in the poem

conflict an internal conflict takes place in the mind of a character who must resolve something. An external conflict takes place between two characters or between a character and a force of nature, society, or the unknown.

dialogue a conversation between characters

fiction an invented story

figurative language words used to say something other than their literal meaning, often to help the reader visualize what is happening. For example, "All the world's a stage."

flashback the return to an event that occurred before the present situation

foreshadowing hints of what is to come

historical document a speech, treaty, memoir, declaration, or other important written document from the past

historical fiction a story or novel whose setting is in some period in the past. Often real people from the past or important historical events are used in works of historical fiction.

imagery the use of vivid description to create pictures, or images, in the reader's mind

metaphor a comparison in which something is said to be something else. Metaphors use *is* or *was*. For example: He is a shining star.

mood the general feeling that an author creates. Mood is created largely through description and setting.

narrator the teller of a story. A first-person narrator tells a story using the word "I."

nonfiction writing about real people and factual events

novel a book-length piece of fiction that usually has a plot and deals with human experience

onomatopoeia the use of a word that sounds like the thing it stands for, such as *buzz* and *sizzle*

personal narrative a true story about a person's life told in the first person

plot what happens in a story, including the problem, the events that lead to solving the problem, and the solution

plot twist a turn of events in a story, novel, or play that is unexpected

poetry literature that uses language chosen for its sound and for its ability to express and evoke emotion

point of view the point from which the story is told. In the **first-person point of view**, the narrator is usually a character in the story. This narrator tells the story by using the pronouns *I* or *we*. In the **third-person point of view**, the narrator may or may not be a character in the story. This narrator uses the pronouns *he*, *she*, or *they*. Sometimes the narrator in the third-person point of view seems to know what every character is thinking and feeling. This narrator is called *omniscient*, or *all-knowing*.

repetition words, phrases, or sentences that are used over and over again

rhyme two or more words that have ending syllables with the same sound

rhythm a regular, repeated pattern of sounds in music or poetry

setting the time and place of a story

short story a brief work of fiction that focuses on one or two main characters and on a single problem

simile a comparison of two unlike things, using the words *like* or *as*. For example: She was as sweet as candy.

stanza a group of two or more lines in a poem that are printed as a unit and held together by length, rhyme scheme, and meter

suspense a state of uncertainty that keeps a reader reading

symbol something that has meaning in itself, but also stands for something else. For example, in a story, a heart may also stand for love.

theme the message that the author wants you to take away from the story. The theme is conveyed by the whole story—by the title, the plot, the characters, the setting, and the mood.

How to Use the Writing Handbook

This handbook includes the writing skills that you mastered in the **rBook**. You can use these directions and charts to review what you know. You can also use them to help you with a new writing assignment.

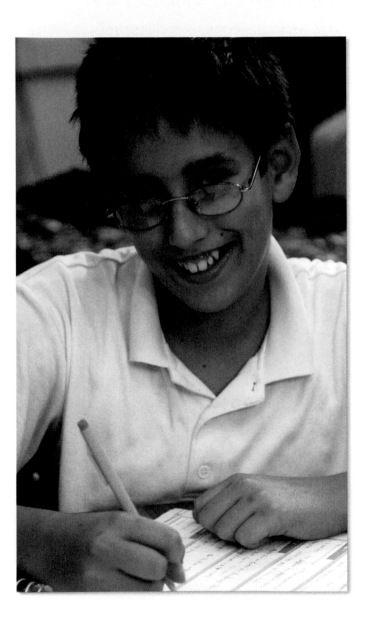

Expository Paragraph

An **expository paragraph** gives information on a topic.

- State the **topic** in the first sentence.
- Use **details** to support or explain the topic.
- Arrange the details in a **logical order**.
- Use **linking words** to connect the ideas.
- **Sum up** or restate the topic in the last sentence.

▶ **Use this chart to plan an expository paragraph.**

Topic Sentence

Detail 1

Detail 2

Detail 3

Conclusion

Expository Summary

A **summary** gives the most important ideas and details from a reading.

- State the **topic of the reading** in the first sentence.
- Include only **important details**.
- Connect the details with **linking words**.
- **Use your own words** in the summary.
- Make sure your summary is **brief, yet complete**.

▶ Use this chart to plan an expository summary.

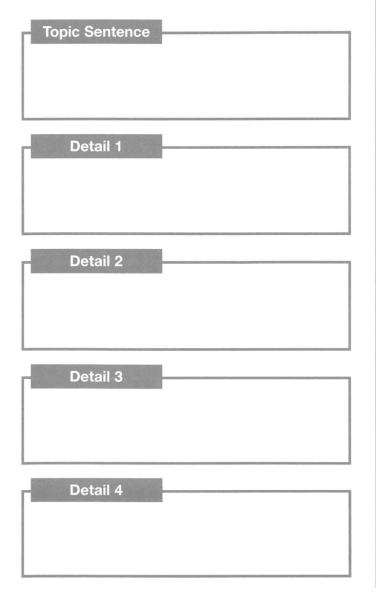

Topic Sentence

Detail 1

Detail 2

Detail 3

Detail 4

Persuasive Paragraph

A **persuasive paragraph** tries to convince the reader to share the writer's opinions.

- State your **opinion** clearly in the first sentence.
- Support your opinion with several **reasons**.
- Make sure that your reasons are **strong and convincing**.
- Use **linking words** to connect your reasons.
- **Restate** your opinion in a concluding sentence.

▶ Use this chart to plan a persuasive paragraph.

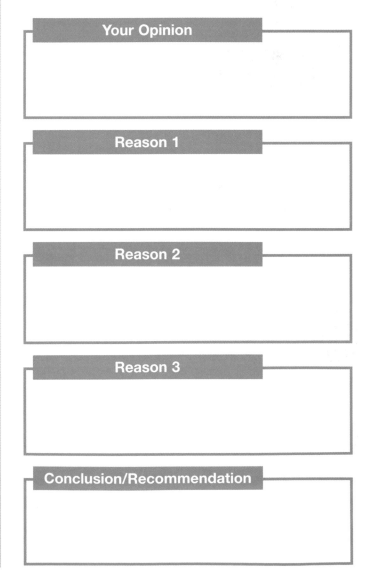

Your Opinion

Reason 1

Reason 2

Reason 3

Conclusion/Recommendation

Narrative Paragraph

A **narrative paragraph** tells a story about an event or a personal experience.

- State the **event** in the beginning.
- Use **details** to tell about the event.
- Arrange the details in the **time order** that they happened.
- Use **linking words** to connect the details.
- **Sum up** the event and tell your feelings about it in the ending.

▶ Use this chart to plan a narrative paragraph.

Event

Detail 1

Detail 2

Detail 3

Ending

Descriptive Paragraph

A **descriptive paragraph** describes a person, place, or thing by offering important details.

- State **what is being described** in the beginning.
- Use **descriptive details** about the subject.
- Make the details as **interesting** as possible.
- Use **linking words** to connect the details.
- **Sum up** the description and your **feelings** about it in the ending.

▶ Use this chart to plan a descriptive paragraph.

Topic Sentence

Detail 1

Detail 2

Detail 3

Conclusion

Literature Response

In a **literature response**, a reader relates a piece of literature to his or her life.

- **Relate your experience** to the main character's experience in the beginning.
- Use **details** to describe that experience.
- Arrange the details in the **time order** they happened.
- Use **linking words** to connect the details.
- **Sum up** your ideas and feelings with the ending.

▶ Use this chart to plan a literature response.

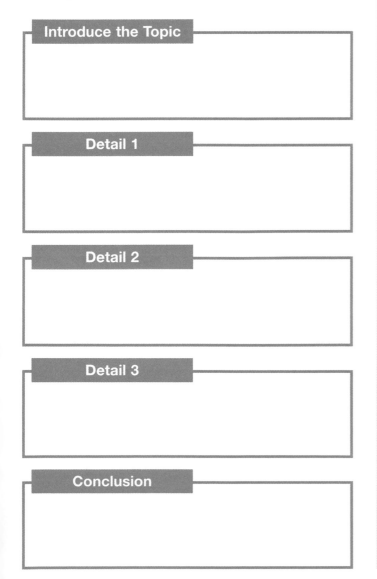

Introduce the Topic

Detail 1

Detail 2

Detail 3

Conclusion

Literature Review

A **literature review** presents the reviewer's opinion of a story.

- State **your opinion** of the story in the beginning.
- Include specific **reasons** that support your opinion.
- Make sure that your reasons are **strong and convincing.**
- Use **linking words** to connect the ideas.
- **Sum up** your opinion with the ending.

▶ Use this chart to plan a literature review.

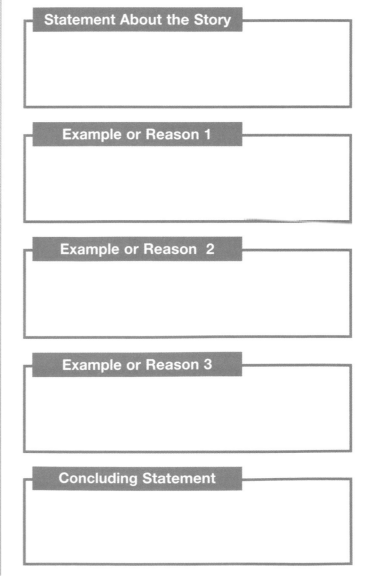

Statement About the Story

Example or Reason 1

Example or Reason 2

Example or Reason 3

Concluding Statement

Grammar

▶ IDENTIFYING SENTENCES AND FRAGMENTS

A **sentence** is a group of words that tells a complete idea. Every sentence has two parts.

- The **subject** tells who or what the sentence is about.
- The **predicate** tells what someone or something does.

A **sentence fragment** is an incomplete sentence that cannot stand by itself. Often, a fragment is missing either a subject or a predicate.

Example

Subject	Predicate
The bears	escaped the fire.
The raging fires	burned everything around them.

▶ CORRECTING SENTENCE FRAGMENTS

A sentence fragment is an incomplete sentence. Often, sentence fragments are missing a subject or a verb. To fix some fragments, add a subject or a verb to make a complete sentence.

Example

Sentence Fragment	Complete Sentence
Settlers from Europe. [missing verb]	Settlers came from Europe.
Moved to America. [missing subject]	Settlers moved to America.

To correct some sentence fragments, you can connect the fragment to a complete sentence by adding a comma and any missing words.

Example

Sentence and Fragment	Complete Sentence
Virpal's mom lived in the United States. Her grandma in India. [missing verb]	Virpal's mom lived in the United States, and her grandma lived in India.

▶ CORRECTING RUN-ON SENTENCES

A run-on sentence is made up of two complete thoughts that are incorrectly joined together.

- To fix a run-on sentence, separate the ideas into two **complete sentences**.
- Or, insert a comma and a connecting word between the thoughts.

Example

Run-on sentence:	Bud woke up late he ran to get in line.
Complete sentences:	Bud woke up late. He ran to get in line.
Complete sentence:	Bud woke up late, so he ran to get in line.

▶ USING CORRECT VERB TENSE

The **tense** of a verb shows when the action happens.

- A present-tense verb shows action that is happening now.
- A past-tense verb shows action that took place in the past. Most past-tense verbs end in *-ed*.

Example

Present-Tense Verb	Past-Tense Verb
Bullies pick on some kids.	Bullies picked on my brother.
A bully teases my friend.	The bully teased her all last year.

▶ USING IRREGULAR VERBS

Most past-tense verbs end in *-ed*. **Irregular verbs** do not.

- You must remember the different spellings of irregular past-tense verbs.
- The verb *to be* is a common irregular verb. Its present-tense forms are *am, is, are*. Its past-tense forms are *was, was, were*.

Example

Present-Tense Verb	Past-Tense Verb
Egyptians make the mummies.	Egyptians made the mummies.
The kings build pyramids.	The kings built pyramids.
The pyramids are made of stone.	The pyramids were made of stone.

▶ SUBJECT-VERB AGREEMENT

The **subject and verb** in a sentence must agree in number.

- A verb that agrees with a singular subject tells what one person, place, or thing is doing. It usually ends in *-s* or *-es*.
- A verb that agrees with a plural subject tells what more than one person or thing is doing. It usually does not end in *-s* or *-es*.

Example

Singular Subject and Verb	Plural Subject and Verb
The marble rolls across the ground.	The marbles roll across the ground.
Lupe squeezes an eraser.	We squeeze erasers, too.

▶ USING SUBJECT AND OBJECT PRONOUNS

A **pronoun** is a word that takes the place of a noun in a sentence.

- Use a subject pronoun in the subject of a sentence.
- Use an object pronoun after a verb or after a word such as *for* or *to*.

Example

Subject Pronoun	Object Pronoun
I have a pet turtle.	My turtle Myrtle likes me.
We found Myrtle in the yard.	Myrtle crawled right up to us.
She eats lettuce for dinner.	Once, I gave a dead fly to her.

▶ USING ADJECTIVES THAT COMPARE

An **adjective** is a word that tells about or describes a noun. Adjectives can help compare two or more people, places, or things.

- To use an adjective to compare two things, add *-er* to the adjective or use the word *more*.
- To use an adjective to compare three or more things, add *-est* to the adjectives or use the word *most*.

Example

Adjective Comparing Two Things	Adjective Comparing Three or More Things
Zac is stronger than his friend.	He is the strongest kid in his class.
Zac is more athletic than his friend.	He is the most athletic student in his class.

▶ USING ADVERBS

An adjective describes a person, place, or thing. An adverb describes a verb, an adjective, or another adverb. Many adverbs end in *-ly*.

- Use an adverb to make your writing more precise.

Example

Adjective	Adverb
Ruby went to a different school.	She was treated differently from whites.
There were unfair laws in many states.	Many people were treated unfairly.
Some brave people demanded justice.	They bravely stood up for their beliefs.

Usage and Mechanics

▶ USING END PUNCTUATION

Different kinds of sentences use different **end punctuation marks**.

- A statement always ends with a period.
- A question always ends with a question mark.

Example

Statement	Question
Firefighters have to be brave.	Do you know a firefighter?
A fire station is down the street.	Have you ever seen a fire?

▶ USING CAPITALS

Some words begin with a **capital letter**.

- The first word in a sentence begins with a capital letter.
- A proper noun begins with a capital letter.

Example

Correct	Incorrect
The girls were all alone.	the girls were all alone.
The guard asked Virpal to stop.	The guard asked virpal to stop.

▶ USING CORRECT WORD ORDER

The **order of words** in a sentence must make sense.

- An adjective comes before the noun it describes.
- A helping verb comes just before the main verb in a statement.

Example

Correct	Incorrect
Bud was a funny kid.	Bud was a kid funny.
Bud liked what he was eating.	Bud liked what was he eating.

▶ USING COMMAS IN A SERIES

Items in a series are separated by **commas**.

- A series is a list of the same kinds of words.
- Commas follow every item in the series except the last one.

Example

Correct	Incorrect
Kids, parents, and teachers all want bullying to end.	Kids parents and teachers all want bullying to end.

▶ USING COMMAS WITH INTRODUCTORY WORDS

A **comma** follows an opening word or phrase at the beginning of a sentence.

- *Yes*, *First*, *Next*, and *Later* are opening words.
- *In addition* and *After a while* are opening phrases.

Example

Correct	Incorrect
Yes, King Tut was a pharaoh. After a while, they found the tomb.	Yes King Tut was a pharaoh. After a while they found the tomb.

▶ USING POSSESSIVES

A **possessive noun** shows ownership.

- Add an apostrophe (') and an *-s* to a singular noun.
- Add an apostrophe to a plural noun that ends in *-s*.

Example

Correct	Incorrect
Lupe's brother gave her advice. She looked at the marbles' colors.	Lupes brother gave her advice. She looked at the marbles colors.

► AVOIDING DOUBLE NEGATIVES

Negatives are words that express *no* or *not*.

- Use only one negative word to express a single negative idea.
- It is incorrect to use two negatives to express a negative idea.

Example

Correct	Incorrect
Tigers should never be pets.	Tigers shouldn't never be pets.
The alligator didn't eat anything.	The alligators didn't eat nothing.

► USING QUOTATION MARKS

Quotation marks show the exact words of a speaker.

- The first word of a quotation is usually capitalized.
- Punctuation usually goes inside the ending quotation mark.

Example

Correct	Incorrect
Annie asked, "Where is the milk?"	Annie asked, "where is the milk?"
"It's in the fridge," Yvonne said.	"It's in the fridge", Yvonne said.

rBook Workshop Log

▶ Fill in the dates that you start and complete each Workshop. Rate your effort during each Workshop using the Rating Guide. Then answer a final question.

Rating Guide

weak	okay	good	great
①	②	③	④

WORKSHOP 1 — Fires Out of Control

Date Started	Date Completed

Self-Assessment
Rate your effort during this Workshop.
① ② ③ ④

What would you do if a fire was headed toward your neighborhood?

_____

_____

_____

WORKSHOP 2 — Coming to America

Date Started	Date Completed

Self-Assessment
Rate your effort during this Workshop.
① ② ③ ④

Which was your favorite article in this Workshop?

❏ "New to the U.S."
❏ "My Journey to America"
❏ "A Nation of Immigrants"

Why? _____

_____

WORKSHOP 3 — Bud, Not Buddy

Date Started	Date Completed

Self-Assessment
Rate your effort during this Workshop.
① ② ③ ④

Do you think the pretend family should have helped Bud? Why or why not?

_____

_____

WORKSHOP 4 — Bullies Beware

Date Started	Date Completed

Self-Assessment
Rate your effort during this Workshop.
① ② ③ ④

What do you think is a good way to stop a bully?

_____

_____

_____

WORKSHOP 5 — Secrets of the Mummy's Tomb

Date Started	Date Completed

Self-Assessment
Rate your effort during this Workshop.
① ② ③ ④

Which of the following things would you most like to see in person?

☐ a mummy

☐ a pyramid

☐ a trap door inside a tomb

WORKSHOP 6 — Good Sports

Date Started	Date Completed

Self-Assessment
Rate your effort during this Workshop.
① ② ③ ④

Would you want to be friends with Lupe? Why or why not?

_____

_____

WORKSHOP 7 — Taming Wild Beasts

Date Started	Date Completed

Self-Assessment
Rate your effort during this Workshop.
① ② ③ ④

Which animal would you least want to own?

☐ a gorilla   ☐ an alligator

☐ a tiger   ☐ a polar bear

Why? _____

_____

WORKSHOP 8 — Food: The Good, the Bad, and the Gross

Date Started	Date Completed

Self-Assessment
Rate your effort during this Workshop.
① ② ③ ④

You know that bugs can be healthy. But would you ever eat one? Why or why not?

_____

_____

WORKSHOP 9 — No Small Hero

Date Started	Date Completed

Self-Assessment
Rate your effort during this Workshop.
① ② ③ ④

If you could ask Ruby Bridges one question, what would you ask her?

_____

_____

Topic Software Log

▶ Use these pages to keep track of the Topic CDs you have completed. Check off each segment you finish. Then, answer a final question about each CD.

Topic CD 1

Can You Believe It?

- ❑ 1.1 Crazy Horse
- ❑ 1.2 Polar Bears
- ❑ 1.3 Art Cars
- ❑ 1.4 I'm No Clown!

The artist or work of art I'd really like to see in person is _____

Topic CD 4

It's How You Play the Game

- ❑ 4.1 No Snow? No Problem!
- ❑ 4.2 On Your Mark
- ❑ 4.3 Let the Games Begin
- ❑ 4.4 Coop Can Shoot

One new thing I learned was _____

Topic CD 2

Predators

- ❑ 2.1 Built to Kill
- ❑ 2.2 Super Senses
- ❑ 2.3 Deadly Droolers
- ❑ 2.4 Dinnertime!

The grossest thing I saw in these videos was _____

Topic CD 5

Thrills and Chills

- ❑ 5.1 Movie Magic
- ❑ 5.2 Do the Math
- ❑ 5.3 Big Spending
- ❑ 5.4 Wild Ride

My favorite segment was _____

Topic CD 3

Mummies, Bones, and Garbage

- ❑ 3.1 The Great Dino Debate
- ❑ 3.2 Mysteries of the Mummy
- ❑ 3.3 Ancient Guards
- ❑ 3.4 Tracing Trash

The most interesting thing I saw on this Topic CD was _____

Topic CD 6

One Man's March: Martin Luther King Jr.

- ❑ 6.1 A Young Man With a Dream
- ❑ 6.2 The Montgomery Bus Boycott
- ❑ 6.3 The March on Washington
- ❑ 6.4 I Have a Dream

The thing I admire most about Martin Luther King Jr. is _____

Topic CD 7

Forgotten Heroes

- ❑ 7.1 Los Mineros
- ❑ 7.2 Playing Hardball
- ❑ 7.3 The Men of the 54th
- ❑ 7.4 Uniting the States

The most heroic group of people in this Topic

CD are _____

_____

Topic CD 8

Weird Science

- ❑ 8.1 Shocking!
- ❑ 8.2 Killer Plants
- ❑ 8.3 Bat Attack
- ❑ 8.4 Winged Wonders

The coolest thing I saw was _____

_____

_____

Topic CD 9

History Mysteries

- ❑ 9.1 Secrets of Stonehenge
- ❑ 9.2 Mayan Mystery
- ❑ 9.3 Lost in Flight
- ❑ 9.4 *Titanic's* Forgotten Sister

The most mysterious story was _____

_____

Topic CD 10

Myths and Monsters

- ❑ 10.1 Phaeton's Wild Ride
- ❑ 10.2 Dragon Tales
- ❑ 10.3 The Legend of Lucia
- ❑ 10.4 Frankenstein Lives!

I think a good movie could be made about

_____

Topic CD 11

It's the *Write* Job

- ❑ 11.1 Sports Report
- ❑ 11.2 Wizard of Words
- ❑ 11.3 Toy Story
- ❑ 11.4 On the Beat

The job I'm most interested in for myself is

_____

_____

Topic CD 12

Beyond Words!

- ❑ 12.1 "The Greatest"
- ❑ 12.2 Under a Spell
- ❑ 12.3 It's a Good Sign
- ❑ 12.4 War of Words

I would recommend this Topic CD to _____

_____

Book Log

▶ Use these pages to keep track of the books you read.

- Write the title in the blank box. Add a design if you like.

- Fill in the date that you started and completed each book.

- Mark what kind of book it was.

- Rate the book using the rating scale at right.
  Then write a statement about the book.

Rating Scale

It was great!	★★★★
It was good.	★★★☆
It was O.K.	★★☆☆
I didn't like it.	★☆☆☆

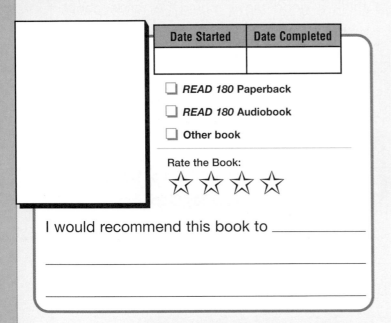

Date Started	Date Completed

☐ *READ 180* Paperback

☐ *READ 180* Audiobook

☐ Other book

Rate the Book:
☆☆☆☆

I would recommend this book to _____

_____

_____

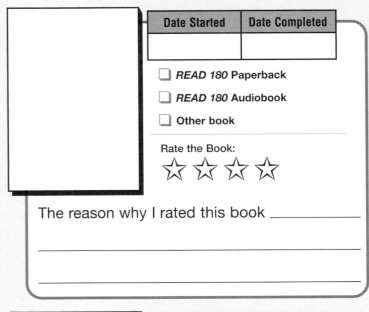

Date Started	Date Completed

☐ *READ 180* Paperback

☐ *READ 180* Audiobook

☐ Other book

Rate the Book:
☆☆☆☆

The reason why I rated this book _____

_____

_____

Date Started	Date Completed

☐ *READ 180* Paperback

☐ *READ 180* Audiobook

☐ Other book

Rate the Book:
☆☆☆☆

This book reminded me of _____

_____

_____

Date Started	Date Completed

☐ *READ 180* Paperback

☐ *READ 180* Audiobook

☐ Other book

Rate the Book:
☆☆☆☆

I chose to read this book because _____

_____

_____

Date Started	Date Completed

- ☐ *READ 180* **Paperback**
- ☐ *READ 180* **Audiobook**
- ☐ **Other book**

Rate the Book:
★ ★ ★ ☆

One question I have for the author is _____

_____

_____

Date Started	Date Completed

- ☐ *READ 180* **Paperback**
- ☐ *READ 180* **Audiobook**
- ☐ **Other book**

Rate the Book:
★ ★ ★ ☆

I think I will/won't remember this book because

_____

_____

Date Started	Date Completed

- ☐ *READ 180* **Paperback**
- ☐ *READ 180* **Audiobook**
- ☐ **Other book**

Rate the Book:
★ ★ ☆ ☆

The best part of this book was _____

_____

_____

Date Started	Date Completed

- ☐ *READ 180* **Paperback**
- ☐ *READ 180* **Audiobook**
- ☐ **Other book**

Rate the Book:
★ ★ ☆ ☆

One new thing I learned in this book was

_____

_____

Date Started	Date Completed

- ☐ *READ 180* **Paperback**
- ☐ *READ 180* **Audiobook**
- ☐ **Other book**

Rate the Book:
☆ ☆ ☆ ☆

If I were making this book into a movie, it would

star _____

_____

Date Started	Date Completed

- ☐ *READ 180* **Paperback**
- ☐ *READ 180* **Audiobook**
- ☐ **Other book**

Rate the Book:
☆ ☆ ☆ ☆

This book was easy/hard to finish because

_____

_____

Student Log

Date Started	Date Completed

- ☐ *READ 180* Paperback
- ☐ *READ 180* Audiobook
- ☐ Other book

Rate the Book:
★ ★ ★ ☆

This book reminded me of _____

_____

_____

Date Started	Date Completed

- ☐ *READ 180* Paperback
- ☐ *READ 180* Audiobook
- ☐ Other book

Rate the Book:
★ ★ ★ ☆

When I first saw this book, I thought it would be

_____

_____

Date Started	Date Completed

- ☐ *READ 180* Paperback
- ☐ *READ 180* Audiobook
- ☐ Other book

Rate the Book:
★ ★ ★ ☆

I would recommend this book to _____

_____

_____

Date Started	Date Completed

- ☐ *READ 180* Paperback
- ☐ *READ 180* Audiobook
- ☐ Other book

Rate the Book:
★ ★ ★ ☆

Reading this book made me feel _____

_____

_____

Date Started	Date Completed

- ☐ *READ 180* Paperback
- ☐ *READ 180* Audiobook
- ☐ Other book

Rate the Book:
★ ★ ★ ☆

The most interesting thing about this book was

_____

_____

Date Started	Date Completed

- ☐ *READ 180* Paperback
- ☐ *READ 180* Audiobook
- ☐ Other book

Rate the Book:
★ ★ ★ ☆

One fact I learned in this book is _____

_____

_____

Date Started	Date Completed

☐ *READ 180* **Paperback**

☐ *READ 180* **Audiobook**

☐ **Other book**

Rate the Book:

☆ ☆ ☆ ☆

The best thing about this book is_____

_____

_____

Date Started	Date Completed

☐ *READ 180* **Paperback**

☐ *READ 180* **Audiobook**

☐ **Other book**

Rate the Book:

☆ ☆ ☆ ☆

Three words that describe this book are

_____

Date Started	Date Completed

☐ *READ 180* **Paperback**

☐ *READ 180* **Audiobook**

☐ **Other book**

Rate the Book:

☆ ☆ ☆ ☆

I would recommend this book to _____

_____

Date Started	Date Completed

☐ *READ 180* **Paperback**

☐ *READ 180* **Audiobook**

☐ **Other book**

Rate the Book:

☆ ☆ ☆ ☆

This book should/should not have a sequel

because_____

_____

Date Started	Date Completed

☐ *READ 180* **Paperback**

☐ *READ 180* **Audiobook**

☐ **Other book**

Rate the Book:

☆ ☆ ☆ ☆

If I were making this book into a movie, it would

star _____

_____

Date Started	Date Completed

☐ *READ 180* **Paperback**

☐ *READ 180* **Audiobook**

☐ **Other book**

Rate the Book:

☆ ☆ ☆ ☆

One new thing I learned in this book is

_____

Keep Track of Your Success!

▶ Create a bar graph showing your SRI Lexile scores over the year.

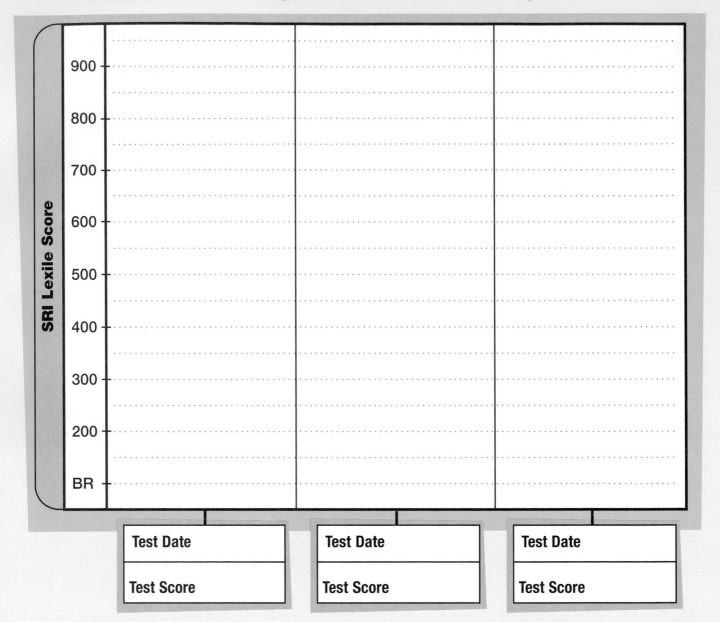

	Test Date
	Test Score

	Test Date
	Test Score

	Test Date
	Test Score

▶ Use this chart to keep track of your *READ 180* rSkills test scores.

	Test 1	Test 2	Test 3	Test 4	Test 5
Test Date					
Test Score					

Grateful acknowledgment is made to the following sources for permission to reprint from previously published material. The publisher has made diligent efforts to trace the ownership of all copyrighted material in this volume and believes that all necessary permissions have been secured. If any errors or omissions have inadvertently been made, proper corrections will gladly be made in future editions.

"Careers: Firefighter" adapted from "A Firefighter in Action" by Jonathan Blum from *Scholastic News* magazine, October 18, 1999. Copyright © 1999 by Scholastic Inc. All rights reserved.

"New to the U.S." adapted from "A New World" by Rebecca Thatcher Murcia from *Scholastic News* Senior Edition magazine, September 29, 2003. Copyright © 2003 by Scholastic Inc. All rights reserved.

"My Journey to America" adapted from "Virpal" from *Scholastic News Online*. Copyright © 2004 by Scholastic Inc. All rights reserved.

Adapted from BUD, NOT BUDDY by Christopher Paul Curtis. Copyright © 1999 by Christopher Paul Curtis. Reprinted by permission of Random House Children's Books, a division of Random House, Inc.

Cover from THE WATSONS GO TO BIRMINGHAM—1963 by Christopher Paul Curtis. Copyright © 1995 by Christopher Paul Curtis. Used by permission of Random House Children's Books, a division of Random House, Inc.

Adapted from "Girl Fight" by Karen Fanning from *Scholastic Choices* magazine, October 2002. Copyright © 2002 by Scholastic Inc. All rights reserved.

"The Marble Champ" from BASEBALL IN APRIL AND OTHER STORIES by Gary Soto. Copyright © 1990 by Gary Soto. Reprinted by permission of Harcourt, Inc.

"Biography of Gary Soto" and author photo from The Official Gary Soto Web Site (http://www.garysoto.com). Reprinted by permission of Gary Soto.

"S-T-R-E-T-C-H" from THE LAST-PLACE SPORTS POEMS OF JEREMY BLOOM by Gordon Korman and Bernice Korman. Copyright © 1996 by Gordon Korman and Bernice Korman. Reprinted by permission of Scholastic Inc. All rights reserved.

"Careers: Veterinary Technician" adapted from "The Veterinary Technician" from *Scholastic Action* magazine, January 21, 2002. Copyright © 2002 by Scholastic Inc. All rights reserved.

Text and cover from THROUGH MY EYES by Ruby Bridges. Copyright © 1999 by Ruby Bridges. Reprinted by permission of Scholastic Press, a division of Scholastic Inc. Cover: AP/Wide World.

"Life Doesn't Frighten Me" from AND STILL I RISE by Maya Angelou. Copyright © 1978 by Maya Angelou. Reprinted by permission of Random House, Inc.

Cover: © Steve Bloom/stevebloom.com, © PhotoLink/Getty Images, © Tom McCarthy/PhotoEdit, Inc., © John Wang/Getty Images, © Terry Froelich/Index Stock Imagery, © Sandro Vannini/Corbis, © Steven K. Doi/Zuma/Corbis, © Michael S. Yamashita/Corbis; p. 2lc: © Michael S. Yamashita/Corbis, bl: © David Young-Wolff/Photo Edit, Inc., Wook-Jin Jung, © John Wang/Getty Images, © Tom McCarthy/PhotoEdit, Inc.; p. 3tl: Aaron Kreielsheimer, lc: © Ace Photo Agency/Robertstock, bl: © Scala/Art Resource, NY; p. 4tl: Jim Cooke, lc: © Steve Bloom/stevebloom.com, bl: © Graham French/Masterfile; p. 5tl: © AP/Wide World Photos; p.6lc: © Michael S. Yamashita/Corbis, rc: Aaron Kreielsheimer, b: © John Wang/Getty Images; p. 7lc: © Science Photo Library/Photo Researchers, Inc., r: © Vincent Pugliese/AP/Wide World Photos, b: Jim Cooke; p. 8–9: © Steven K. Doi/Zuma/Corbis; p. 9tr: © Jim Zuckerman/Corbis; p. 10: John McColgan/National Interagency Fire Center; p. 11: © Rubberball Productions/Getty Images; p. 12: © Bruce Chambers/Orange County Register/Corbis; p. 13tr: © Mike McMillan-Spotfire Images; p. 14: © Michael S. Yamashita/Corbis; p. 15t: © Rubberball Productions/Getty Images; p.16: © Dana R. Bowler/Ventura County Star/Corbis; p.20 bl: © John Wang/Getty Images, ct: © Marc Romanelli/Getty Images, cb: © Michael Kelley/Getty Images; p.21br: © Photodisc via SODA; p.23bl: © Royalty-Free/Corbis, tl: © Michael S. Yamashita/Corbis, tr:© Jim Zuckerman/Corbis, br: © Richard T. Nowitz/Corbis; p.28l: Tim McKinney, r: © Bill Stormont/Corbis; p. 29: © Rubberball Productions/Getty Images; p.32bl: © Rudi Von Briel/PhotoEdit, Inc., tl: © Terry Froelich/Index Stock Imagery, tlc: © Mary Kate Denny/PhotoEdit, Inc., tcr: © Rudi Von Briel/PhotoEdit, Inc., tr: © Tom McCarthy/PhotoEdit, Inc., br: © Spencer Platt/Getty Images, bc: © Terry Froelich/Index Stock Imagery, c: © David Young-Wolff/Photo Edit, Inc., ct: Wook-Jin Jung, cr: © John Wang/Getty Images, background: Jim McMahon; p. 33: © Kevin Dodge/Masterfile; p. 34br: Michael Pilla; pp. 36–37t: Jim McMahon; p. 37: Courtesy Virpal; p. 38t: © GeneralStockOne/Alamy, inset: Courtesy Virpal; p. 40: © Steve Allen/Brand X Pictures; p. 41br: © Bettmann/Corbis; p. 43tl: © Kevin Dodge/Masterfile; p. 44bl: © David Young-Wolff/Photo Edit, Inc., tr: © Royalty-Free/Corbis; p.45lc: © Photodisc via SODA, ltc: Rushmoor Borough Council, UK, tr: © Jeanne White/Photo Researchers, Inc.; p. 46r: © John Wang/Getty Images; p. 47bl: © dk & Dennie Cody/Masterfile, tl: © Dugald Bremner/Getty Images, tr: David Young-Wolff/PhotoEdit, Inc. br: © Nancy Sheehan/PhotoEdit, Inc.; p. 52bl: © Jack Dempsey/AP/Wide World Photos, tr: © Mark Petersson/Corbis; p. 54: Michael Pilla; p. 57: © David Young-Wolff/PhotoEdit, Inc.; p. 72 bl: © Peter Menzel/Menzel Photography/menzelphoto.com, tr: © Jim Cummins/Getty Images; p. 73lc: © Mel Yates/Getty Images, r: © Robert Daly/Getty Images; p. 75bl: © Michael Newman/PhotoEdit, Inc., tl: © Left Lane Productions/Corbis, tr: © Guy Cali/Stock Connection, br: © Steve Skjold/Alamy; p. 80: Paul Keyser; p. 84–85: © Ace Photo Agency/Robertstock; p. 85: © Michelle D. Bridwell/PhotoEdit, Inc.; p. 86: © Bob Daemmrich/The Image Works; p. 87: © Tony Freeman/PhotoEdit, Inc.; p. 89: © Richard Hutchings/PhotoEdit, Inc.; p. 90tr: Cleo Photography/PhotoEdit, Inc.; p. 92r: © Dick Makin/Getty Images; p. 95t: © www.imagesource.com/Alamy; p. 96bl: © Rudi von Briel/PhotoEdit, Inc., tr: © Terje Rakke/Getty Images; p.97b: © Ariel Skelley/Corbis; p. 99bl: © Steve Skjold/PhotoEdit, Inc., tl: © Bob Daemmrich/The Image Works, tr: © Mary Kate Denny/PhotoEdit, Inc., br: © Rubberball Productions/PictureQuest; p. 104t & b: Kelly LaDuke © Scholastic Inc.; p. 105t: Public Information Office, City of Jacksonville, FL; p. 106br: © Bob Daemmrich/The Image Works; p. 108–109: Scala/Art Resource, NY; p. 109: © Larry Lee Photography/Corbis; p. 110: © Sandro Vannini/Corbis; p. 111b: © Photos.com Select/IndexOpen; p. 112–113t: © Science Photo Library/Photo Researchers, Inc.; p. 113b: © Thomas Hartwell/Corbis; p. 114tr: © Vincent Yu/AP/Wide World Photos; p.116–117: Sekai Bunka/Premium/Panoramic Images/NGSImages.com; p. 117inset: Mary Evans Picture Library; p. 118rc: © Vanni/Egyptian Museum/Art Resource, NY; p.120 bl: © Brand X Pictures/PictureQuest, tc: © Neal Preston/Corbis, tr: © David Young-Wolff/PhotoEdit, Inc.; p. 121tl: © Wolfgang Kaehler, tr: © Michael Newman/PhotoEdit, Inc.; p. 122tr: © Richard T. Nowitz/Corbis; p. 123bl: © Margot Granitsas /The Image Works, tl: © Yann Arthus-Bertrand/Corbis; tr: © Thomas Hartwell/Corbis, br: © Jeff Greenberg/PhotoEdit, Inc.; p. 128bl: © Doug Page/Index Stock Imagery, tr: © Royalty-Free/Corbis; p. 129tr: Paul Edmondson/Getty Images; p.130: © Thomas Hartwell/Corbis; p. 133r: © David Young-Wolff/PhotoEdit, Inc.; p. 150–151: © Ken Ruinard/Anderson Independent-Mail, S.C./AP/Wide World Photos; p. 152l: Lon C. Diehl/PhotoEdit, Inc., tr: © Joe Patronite/Getty Images, br: © Michelle Bridwell/PhotoEdit, Inc.; p. 153lc: © Bud Freund/IndexOpen, tlc: © Shmuel Thaler/IndexOpen, tr: © Jim Cummins/Getty Images; p. 160 & 161: Courtesy Gary Soto; p. 164–165: © Steve Bloom/stevebloom.com; p. 164l: © Reuters/Corbis, r: © Michael Oates/Zuma Press p.165rc: © Steve Bloom/stevebloom.com; p. 166t: NYPD/AP/Wide World Photos; p. 167background: © John Chellman/Animals Animals; p. 168–169: © Jeff Holt; p. 170tr: © Ariel Skelley/Corbis; p. 171b: © Gary Braasch/Zuma Press; p. 172r: © D. DeMello/Wildlife Conservation Society; p.174rc: © Vincent Pugliese/AP/Wide World Photos, b: © Wildlife Conservation Society/Bronx Zoo; p. 176bl: David Young-Wolff/Photo Edit, Inc., cr: © Michael Kelley/Getty Images, tr: © Tim Flach/Getty Images; p. 177bl: © Wolfgang Kaehler, tl: © David Frazier/The Image Works; p. © Chris McGrath/Getty Images; p. 178: © James Balog/Getty Images; p. 179bl: © Dan Riedlhuber /Reuters, tl: © Hubert Klein/Peter Arnold, Inc., tr: © Steve Bloom/stevebloom.com, br: © Christine Kolisch/Corbis; p. 184tr & bl: © Stan Godlewski; p. 188–189: © Graham French/Masterfile; p. 189br: © Royalty-Free/Corbis; p.190: © David Kohl/AP/Wide World Photos; p. 191b: © Photos.com Select/IndexOpen; p. 192: © Peter Menzel/Menzel Photography/menzelphoto.com; p. 194tr: © Peter Menzel/Menzel Photography/menzelphoto.com; p. 195b: © Photos.com Select/IndexOpen; p. 196r: Sherie Steinberg Kote for Better Nutrition Magazine; p. 199b: © Rhoda Sidney/Photo Edit, Inc.; p.200bl: © Richard Hutching/Photo Edit, Inc., tr: © MonkeyApple/Greatstock Photographic Library/Alamy; p. 201btl: © Myrleen Ferguson Cate/Photo Edit, Inc., tr: Holos/Getty Images, b: © Digital Vision; p. 203bl: © Burke/Triolo/ Brand X Pictures/ PictureQuest, tl: © Stockbyte/PictureQuest, tr: © Burke/Triolo/ Brand X Pictures/ PictureQuest, br: © David Young-Wolff/PhotoEdit, Inc., c: © C Squared Studios/Getty Images; p. 208t & b: © Bob Daemmrich; p. 209b: © Becky Luigart-Stayner/Corbis; p. 210br: © Peter Menzel/Menzel Photography/menzelphoto.com; p. 212–213: © AP/Wide World Photos; p. 213: © Gabe Palmer/Corbis; p. 214t: © Bettmann/Corbis; p. 216r: © Bettmann/Corbis; p. 218tr: © Bettmann/Corbis; p. 221b: © Bettmann/Corbis; p. 223t: © AP/Wide World Photos; p. 224bl: © John Rooney/AP/Wide World Photos, bc: © Photodisc via SODA, br: © Bettmann/Corbis; p. 225bl: © Bettmann/Corbis; p. 226tr: Mark Melham, *Chloe in the Morning*/www.artandwriting.org via SODA; p.228lc: © Duomo/Corbis, tr: © Tim Boyle/Getty Images, bc: James Levin via SODA; p. 229bl: © Stephen Dalton/Photo Researchers, Inc., lc: James Levin via SODA; p. 231bl: © Spencer Grant/Photo Edit, Inc., tl: © Jonathan Nourok/Photo Edit, Inc., tr: © David Young-Wolff/Photo Edit, Inc., br: © Michael DeYoung/Corbis; p. 236tr: Paul Horton/Connecticut College; p. 237rc: © Denise Truscello/WireImage.com, cl: © Virginia Sherwood/ABC, Inc., cr: © MLB Photos; p. 238br: © Bettmann/Corbis; p. 240br: © Tony Freeman/Photo Edit, Inc.; p. 241bl: © Bob Daemmrich/PhotoEdit, Inc.; p. 242b: © Mary Kate Denny/PhotoEdit, Inc.; p. 243l: © Michael Newman/PhotoEdit, Inc.; p. 244tl: © Photodisc via SODA, br: © Michael Newman/PhotoEdit, Inc.; p. 245br: © MonkeyApple/Greatstock Photographic Library/Alamy; p. 246tc: © Bob Daemmrich/PhotoEdit Inc., p. 247br: © Photodisc via SODA; p. 248lc: © H. Kehrer/zefa/Masterfile; p. 249lc: © Bob Daemmrich/The Image Works, tr: © Doug Scott/age fotostock; p. 250l: © Roger Wyan; p. 258l: © Dennie Cody; p268tl: © Michael S. Yamashita/Corbis, lct: © David Young-Wolff/Photo Edit, Inc., Wook-Jin Jung, © John Wang/Getty Images, © Tom McCarthy/PhotoEdit, Inc., lcb: Aaron Kreielsheimer, bl: © Ace Photo Agency/Robertstock; p. 269tl: © Scala/Art Resource, NY, lct: Jim Cooke, lc: © Steve Bloom/stevebloom.com, lcb: © Graham French/Masterfile, bl: © AP/Wide World Photos.

"Bud, Not Buddy": Aaron Kreielsheimer © Scholastic Inc.

"Good Sports": Jim Cooke © Scholastic Inc.